L E

OF POWER

Take Control of Alcohol, Drugs and Your Life

Robert Schwebel, Ph.D.
Author of The Seven Challenges Program

VIVA PRESS

Viva Press
PO Box 57621
Tucson, AZ 85732

Counselors and organizations interested in providing The Seven Challenges® program can obtain information about training and authorization at sevenchallenges.com.

For information about arranging speaking engagements by the author, find contact information at sevenchallenges.com

Book design by Katherine Smith
Cover design by Robert Jaime

ISBN 978-1-890164-01-0 (paperback)
ISBN 978-1-890164-02-7 (e-book)

10 9 8 7 6 5 4 3 2 1

Addiction. Self-help. Recovery. Psychology.

Note to Readers

This book is intended to be educational in nature, and not a substitute for psychotherapy or appropriate medical care. The ideas and suggestions are written for a general audience and cannot be considered to be the professional advice or recommendation of a psychologist because that must be individualized and involve a personal consultation. You, the reader, are responsible for your own decisions about how to behave. The author and publisher assume no responsibility and no liability for your decisions and what may arise as a result of using the information in this book. Professional consultation with a healthcare professional may be indicated. This book is not a substitute for that.

CONTENTS

INTRODUCTION & CHALLENGE ONE

Challenging yourself to honestly look at your life, including your use of alcohol and other drugs

LEAP OF POWER

You may have been told that you are powerless over alcohol and other drugs. You may even feel that way yourself. Well, I've got some very good news for you: You absolutely are not powerless. Right now, you can take a *leap of power* and gain control over drugs and the rest of your life. Millions of people with very serious drug problems, including addiction, have done it. I'm not assuming all readers of this book have a drug problem. If you're uncertain whether you do or don't, you'll get a chance to figure it out for yourself as you continue reading. But if you do have a drug problem, even if you feel frustrated and overwhelmed, you can take the leap.

Many people read a book like this when their lives are in disarray. They may feel hopeless, confused, and tempted to give up. Some may even desperately crave drugs and feel that they can't make it through the day without them. A leap of power means rising above your situation and what you feel at the time. It's about believing *the possibility* that somewhere within yourself, you have the power and energy to step up to the plate and make things right. Even if you doubt yourself and don't feel that you can do it, I'm telling you right now that you can. I've seen it time and time again. People grit their teeth, decide they want a better life, and say, "I'm going for it." They take a leap of power and surprise the doubters and even themselves.

I won't pretend that it's easy. If you have a serious drug problem and decide to quit or set new limits, it will be a huge challenge with no quick fix. I'm certain there will be mistakes and setbacks along the way. It will be important to draw upon all available resources including the possibility of counseling and the use of medication to assist you. However, there is no substitute for your own power and persistence. You can do it. As you read this book, you will see there are ways to organize your efforts, prepare, stay focused and do what we all must do: learn from mistakes and keep improving.

Some people are quite certain and may have been told that if they take one sip of alcohol or the slightest amount of another drug they will lose control, feel powerless, and won't be able to stop. Even in such circumstances, these individuals still have the power within themselves to *not* take the first sip or the slightest amount. They are not powerless. The last thing people need when they are feeling weak and vulnerable is to doubt their personal power, even when it comes to alcohol, the opioids, crack, and all the other drugs.

I HOPE YOU'LL LIKE THIS BOOK

You're probably reading this book for one or more of these reasons.

1. You're concerned about your use of alcohol or other drugs; either wondering if you have a problem or convinced that you do.
2. Someone who cares about you thinks you have a problem with alcohol or other drugs and has given you this book.
3. Someone who has authority over you, such as an employer, judge, or probation officer has sent you to a counselor or counseling agency that uses this book.

Whatever your reasons, I hope you'll like what you read and benefit from it.

If *you are concerned* about your use of alcohol or other drugs, I think you'll find this book offers a respectful way to look at your life, including your drug use, without telling you what to do. You make the decisions. If you want to make changes, it will help you succeed. If you've had difficulty changing in the past – even repeated setbacks and failure – don't give up. You can learn from previous experience, consider new options, apply new ideas, and succeed this time.

If *someone who cares about you is concerned* about your use of alcohol or other drugs, this person could be right...or wrong. If you are open-minded – which is a good thing to be – and want to evaluate this matter yourself, you should find this book helpful. If, at the end, you don't want to make changes, at least you'll know that you carefully thought about it and didn't simply rush to defend yourself.

If *you are being forced to read this book* because you're in a drug program, I'm sorry about that. It never feels good to be forced to do anything. However, I hope you'll be pleasantly surprised to see that this book offers a respectful way to look at your life, including your drug use – without judgments, put downs, or pressure of any sort.

NOTE: Throughout this book I'll be talking about alcohol and other drugs. To simplify, I'll often just say "drugs." Alcohol is a drug, but people sometimes forget that. Occasionally, I'll use the expression "alcohol and other drugs" as a reminder.

JUDGMENTAL PEOPLE

The general public can be very harsh, critical, and judgmental about drugs. You've probably heard the putdowns that say or imply that people who use drugs are one or more of the following: irresponsible; weak-willed; moral failures; selfish pleasure-seekers; conformists who can't say no; or stupid losers who aren't smart enough to see the harm.

I can assure you that you won't be judged or put down in this book. There's no blaming and finger pointing. In fact, this book recognizes that people use drugs for a wide variety of valid reasons that can be entirely understood without blaming and shaming them, and without passing moral judgments.

There are many benefits to drug use, as well as many risks. This book will support you in making your own informed decisions about drugs. If you want to make changes in your life, it will help you find your own course of action and succeed with it.

BOSSY PEOPLE

The general public tends to get pretty bossy toward individuals who are using drugs. They tell them that they have a problem and need to quit. They bombard them with lectures about drug dangers or with a barrage of clever questions designed to convince them they have a serious problem. They argue, often dogmatically, that there is only one solution for everyone, abstinence, which isn't true. It's the right choice for some people, but not everyone. Other people with drug problems have the power to decrease their use and stay within the limits they set for themselves.

Bossy pressure stirs up resistance. No one wants to be criticized, told what to do, or backed into a corner. Many people fight back and defend their drug use. Then they are told: "You are defensive. You are in denial." This creates even more resentment. Sometimes, though, to put an end to the drama, people simply fake it by saying that they're going to quit, though they have no such intentions.

You may expect that a book like this is going to argue a point: Maybe try to convince you to quit or at least cut back. Maybe harp on the dangers of drugs. Maybe assume that you have a problem. There is *no* hidden agenda in this book; *no* attempt to convince you that you have a problem; *no one* telling you that you must change and dictating what this change will look like. It's not an *intervention* with a room full of people ranting and "laying it on the line." There's no shame. No blame. No passing judgment. No one telling you what to do.

I wrote this book to provide a free-thinking zone; to help you organize your own thoughts about your life and use of drugs; and to support you in making your own wise decisions. You'll have an opportunity to consider the benefits and harm from your drug use; the role that drugs play in your life; and the options available to you. In the end, you draw your own conclusions – whatever they may be. If you conclude that you have a drug problem and want to change, you decide how to proceed and when to start. Many people overcome drug problems by committing to abstinence. Many people do it by setting new limits and adhering to them. Readers of this book are encouraged to determine for themselves which strategy works best for them in their own lives. If right now, or at any point, you believe you have a problem and want to set new limits or quit, you'll find guidance and support on these pages.

BLESSING AND BURDEN

I'm guessing that you'll be pleased that the words on these pages are not yet another "voice" ranting at you and telling you what to do about drugs. Of course, that puts the burden on you. You have to think things through for yourself and make your own decisions about your life, including your use of alcohol and other drugs. It makes sense: You know yourself best. You're the most affected by the decisions. You have the most at stake.

Leap of Power challenges you to do the work of honestly and carefully thinking about your life; making your own decisions; successfully following through on whatever you decide; and holding yourself accountable.

Some people have tried to change and failed in their attempts. They may have "lost everything" and feel powerless. This doesn't mean that they are powerless. This means they need to figure out what has stood in their way. If this has been your experience, you'll find help in figuring out the obstacles and overcoming them. You'll see some of the subtleties that are typically ignored in making decisions to change, the importance of preparation, the need for determination, the value of support, and the type of self-monitoring and problem solving that will help you achieve success. You can find solutions that work for you. But remember this: Change takes practice. It's important to persevere with your effort because your life will be a whole lot better when you overcome a drug problem.

SO, WHO WROTE THIS, AND WHAT'S IT ALL ABOUT?

On these first few pages, I keep saying "I," so maybe you've been wondering who is this "I?"

Well, I'm an old and very unconventional psychologist who has been working with people who have alcohol and other drug problems for almost 50 years, starting even before I got my Ph.D. I've helped people overcome everything ranging from serious, long standing addictions to minor (but pesky) drug problems. Early on I saw, beyond a shadow of doubt, that people could overcome drug problems and lead healthy, satisfying lives. It also seemed obvious to me, though professionals have been slow to recognize this, that people use drugs for a reason – to satisfy or attempt to satisfy personal needs. If they stop relying on drugs for this, they have to find other ways to meet these needs, or learn to live without them being met. In short, this means that people who are overcoming drug problems must also make changes in the "rest of their lives." For the past 25 years, I have been training counselors across the country to use The Seven Challenges®, a comprehensive counseling program for people with drug problems.

Nobody has a perfect life. We all have issues. People who want to take charge of their own lives must work on their personal issues to make thing better. My profession (psychology) speaks about diagnoses of mental illness and mental disorders. Although this has some value in some circumstances, it also misses something important: The personal problems of individuals can never be reduced to these oversimplified categories. Our problems are complex. They're the product of our experiences in families and communities, which in turn, are strongly influenced by the conditions in which we live. So, you'll find no diagnoses in this book, and no talk of mental illness or mental disorders. Rather, this book offers you an opportunity to look at the issues in your personal life that matter to you, take control of things, and make changes *without* any label or stigma.

I offer no easy solution. Sometimes people with drug problems are miserably depressed or terribly anxious; or have serious relationship or family problems; or have severely low self-esteem; or big trouble managing emotions. Sometimes, they've lost their family, home and job. If they want to overcome drug problems, they have to work on these other issues as well. This book is for self-help. I never want to underestimate what people can do on their own with dedicated effort and willpower. By the same token, support is invaluable. Furthermore, I don't want to pretend that this book can solve all your problems. On these pages you'll find suggestions that you focus on certain problems. At times, you may be thinking: "I don't have any idea how to do this." That's why I often mention the possibility of seeking good, skilled counseling from a non-judgmental person. This book can be a valuable complement to counseling. At a minimum, I hope it will be inspirational and get you started. With or without help, you will have to invest a huge effort if you want to take a leap of power and overcome drug problems. You can do it. You can take control of your own life.

THE SEVEN CHALLENGES®

To make things simple, each chapter of this book is based on one of the critical challenges in making informed decisions about drugs ... and succeeding with them. There are seven challenges and therefore seven chapters. The challenges are listed below and briefly described.

CHALLENGE ONE: Challenging yourself to honestly look at your life, including your use of alcohol and other drugs
This is crucial to all that follows. You need to be brutally honest in looking at your life so you can figure out what's really happening and make the best possible decisions.

CHALLENGE TWO: Challenging yourself to look at what you like about alcohol and other drugs, and why you use them
In making decisions about drugs, you need to consider what you like about them. This explains why you use them and what you would be giving up if you decide to quit (or use less).

CHALLENGE THREE: Challenging yourself to look at harm that has happened and could happen from your use of alcohol and other drugs
In making decisions about drugs, you need to consider the harm from your use of them, and the potential harm if you are doing risky things.

CHALLENGE FOUR: Challenging yourself to look at your responsibility and the responsibility of others for your problems
This is about shared responsibility – not excessively blaming and shaming yourself for drug or any other problems, and not blaming only the world for everything (which would leave you with nothing you could do about it).

CHALLENGE FIVE: Challenging yourself to look at where you are headed, where you would like to go, and what you would like to accomplish
This is about your direction in life: what is important to you, what you value, and what you want for yourself. You're in charge. In making drug decisions, it's important to think about how drugs will affect your future.

CHALLENGE SIX: Challenging yourself to make thoughtful decisions about your life, including your use of alcohol and other drugs
This is where you put it all together and make informed decisions.

CHALLENGE SEVEN: Challenging yourself to take action and succeed with your decisions about your life and use of alcohol and other drugs
This is about following through – taking action to make sure you succeed, and dealing with setbacks along the way. This is the ultimate goal: Taking action to overcome drug problems and improve your life.

Each chapter of this book is about one of the challenges. Each concludes with a summary, listing the actions you can take to follow through with the ideas that were presented. The summary will help clarify your thinking about the content you read and give you a chance to decide if, and how, you might want to act on it.

NO TIME TO SPARE

I wanted to write a short book that cuts to the chase, so readers could pick it up and quickly get the help they needed. You can see, though, that going through the challenges to make fully informed decisions about alcohol and other drugs takes time. Plus, you not only have to deal with drugs, but also everything else in your life. Therefore, the book is not as thin as I had hoped.

Nevertheless, people sometimes don't have the luxury of time to think deeply about their drug use, consider all the available options, and prepare for success. They feel that they must do something immediately – either set limits or quit. Sometimes this is their own choice because something bad just happened or because they've had a long history of negative consequences from drug use. These people want to make changes right now because they want the harm to go away.

Sometimes people decide to immediately quit or set limits on their drug use for a very different reason – in response to pressure. They feel they must act right away because trouble looms over the horizon. They are in danger of losing a spouse (or romantic partner), a job, child custody, or something else important. Many people quit or cut back because of legal matters – diversion, probation, parole, or drug court. This doesn't necessarily mean admitting to a drug problem. Rather, they are admitting to a problem with a spouse (or romantic partner), employer, or court authority that happens to involve drugs. It doesn't mean a forever decision. Maybe a person wants to change drug use behavior only until probation is over. Or, until he or she is through with drug court, or until things get better at home or on the job.

Whether it is to stop the harm right now or to get out of trouble, people make quick decisions to set limits or quit. Because these are better described as an impulse to change rather than a fully informed decision, the challenge to succeed with them is more difficult. Nevertheless, it can be done. **Readers of this book who want to immediately set new limits or quit using drugs should read the rest of this chapter; then jump right away to Challenge Seven (page 115) and start to apply what they learn on those pages.** If you're aching for action, Challenge Seven provides step-by-step suggestions about quitting or setting limits. It will give you a flying start. You'll get a sense of when, where, why, with whom, etc., you get into trouble with drugs, and what you can do right now to stop the problem.

If you skip ahead to Challenge Seven after you finish this chapter, I urge you to then return to Challenge Two and read it and all the challenges that follow. There's no shortcut. These challenges lay the foundation for making fully informed decisions about drugs and "the rest of your life;" a necessity for enduring success. You may want to skip them. Please don't. One of the biggest obstacles to overcoming drug problems is that people rush to change without adequate preparation. *It's very important to read the earlier chapters and do the hard work that builds the foundation for sustaining long-term success.*

THE BENEFITS OF ALCOHOL AND OTHER DRUGS

Anyone with an open mind can see that there are benefits from drug use. (Challenge Two is all about this.)

Usually, people start using drugs because they're curious and have an opportunity to try them. Some people don't like the effects very much. Others like the effects. They see that drugs can provide pleasure. Drugs can be fun, exciting, and even thrilling. They can be a social activity – something to do with friends. They can change how the world looks. They can help you forget problems. They can change your mood. Some drugs calm you down. Others give you a burst of energy. They can relieve physical and emotional pain. They can turn off unpleasant thoughts. They can be an escape from daily reality. They can help you cope with stress. Drugs can help you sleep. They can lift inhibitions and give you "courage" to do things you wouldn't readily do if you were not under the influence. No wonder people use them!

In short, drugs can be an enormous source of pleasure and provide great relief from pain or other distress. Many people like the benefits. Some like them so much that they use a lot of drugs.

THE HARM FROM ALCOHOL AND OTHER DRUGS

Just as there is a good side to drugs, there are some risks as well. Not everyone who uses drugs has problems with them, but some people do, and sometimes the problems are serious. (Challenge Three is all about the harm from drugs.)

When thinking about harm from alcohol and other drugs, people tend to focus on heavy, daily use. However, drug problems can occur when they are used rarely, infrequently, sporadically, or even during a single incident: Drugs can interfere with good judgment and lead you to do crazy, embarrassing, irresponsible, dangerous, and stupid things. This can affect your love life, marriage, family, health, employment, financial status, reputation, education, and social life.

Drugs can have unintended side effects. For example: When used to avoid or escape reality, they can keep you from *confronting and solving* important problems that should be addressed, or from *learning other ways of coping* with life's problems.

Frequent use of drugs increases the risks of harm. Drugs can harm your body in numerous ways – some immediate and some long term – depending upon the specific drug, the quantity, and a variety of other factors. A serious drug habit can be expensive. Some people commit crimes to pay for drugs, or compromise themselves in other ways to attain them.

The level of drug use can even reach the point of dependence, or as it is often called: addiction. When this happens, people may want to quit, but feel that they can't. They may try to quit, but fail.

Some people have an ongoing back-and-forth struggle to control their drug use. They are drug-free and sober for a period of time, but then slip. Or they use drugs mostly at low levels, but occasionally go to excess.

Finally, because certain drugs are illegal, the use of these drugs can also have legal consequences.

EVERYTHING ELSE IN YOUR LIFE (BESIDES DRUGS)

One of the stupidest things about "Just Say NO" is the idea that drug use stands apart from the rest of a person's life: just a bad behavior that can be eliminated with a simple action (Saying NO). Kind of like popping a pimple.

This way of thinking bears no resemblance to reality. Drug use has everything to do with whatever else is going on in a person's life. People use drugs to satisfy, or attempt to satisfy, personal needs of all sorts. Drugs provide pleasure. They also relieve distress from negative thoughts, emotions, and experiences. You can't understand your own drug use without considering all the circumstances and conditions that surround it.[1]

If now or at some point in the future you want to set new limits or quit using drugs, then you'll need to think seriously about everything else in your life (besides drugs) in order to maintain long-term success. You'll have to learn to live with unmet needs or find new ways to satisfy them. You'll have to develop other ways to find pleasure. You'll probably have to increase your ability to prevent, solve, or cope with problems. You'll have to learn to tolerate unpleasant emotions – the ones you wish would go away. If you make changes in your drug use behavior, you'll also have to make corresponding changes in your lifestyle. Furthermore, there may not be any perfect substitute for the pleasure and relief from pain that drugs provide. You may have to let go of certain benefits; make some sacrifices. It's your choice: Keep using without new limits, or set new limits, or quit.

MASTERY LIVING

The guiding principle in this book is based on the idea I call Mastery Living; a way of life that is practiced by people who want to take charge of their own destiny. They pay attention and think carefully about what is happening in their lives. Whatever is going well, they appreciate and leave alone. Whatever is not going well or as well as they would like, they confront. These are their "issues." They work on whatever issues are most important to them. They confront any obstacles or problems that stand in their way to

[1] *Stanton Peele, Claude Steiner and Andrew Weil wrote about this more than four decades ago.*

a good life…and persist until they master them.

The starting assumptions of Mastery Living are:

- We all have obstacles and problems in life.
- It is important to identify and confront our obstacles and problems.
- Obstacles and problems can be overcome.

This is a powerful "you can do it" approach to life. You can always take action to make things better. Mastery Living is a way to take control of your own life, including your drug use. If you don't take control, then surely you will drift without direction, and circumstances or other people will control you.

I would like to echo the words of Christopher Robin in *Pooh's Great Adventure*. He said: "You're braver than you believe, stronger than you seem, and smarter than you think."

As you gain mastery over your life, you will be constantly bombarded with decisions to make about how to proceed. Wise decision-making is an important part of Mastery Living.

APPLYING THE MASTERY APPROACH TO DRUGS

A mastery approach to life includes looking closely at your drug use, and then deciding for yourself whether you have problems or not, and what you want to do.

As much as a person may like the pleasure and relief that come from drugs, there is also a potential for problems. Some people have no problems. Some people have minor problems. Some people have major problems. Some have problems only with certain drugs or under certain conditions. Some may not have problems with drugs *per se*, but recognize that they have problems with the courts or other authorities that involve drugs (for example, abstinence as a condition of probation or continued employment).

If you think you have a drug problem, then it is an issue you should address. Mastery Living, as applied to drugs, is an optimistic approach based on the assumption that you can set your mind to overcoming it, and do so successfully. If you are willing to work hard you can accomplish whatever you set out to do. But this approach is not for the faint of heart. This is a book of challenges, not promises.

LYING TO YOURSELF

In evaluating your own drug use, be careful to guard against lying to yourself. Many people who actually have a problem with alcohol or other drugs fall in this trap. They say that everything is OK.

"I don't have a problem."
"I can stop whenever I want."
"No big deal. I know what I'm doing."

Some people lie to themselves by saying "I don't care," when really they do, but can't admit it. Even when bad things have happened to them at home, at work, with their health, with friends, with family, and in their loving relationships, they rationalize and make excuses for everything. For example:

"I've been overdoing it with drugs, but only because I have other problems."
"I know people who use a lot more drugs than I do."

They keep saying that things will get better, but they don't. They say they can control their use, but haven't been able to do so. They believe what they want to believe[2], not necessarily what the evidence indicates. Then, when someone says to them that they have a problem, they simply deny it.

They reply: "It's not my problem – it's yours."

If they want to gain mastery over their lives, they must face up to reality.

WHAT IF THE BUBBLE BURST?

Considering all the shaming and blaming from the public, it's not surprising that many people who actually have problems with alcohol and other drugs lie to themselves. It's a protective mechanism.

Another reason that people lie to themselves about drugs is because they're afraid to face what they might find if they took an

[2] *Much like Stephen Colbert's definition of "truthiness;" believing one's own thinking, despite facts and evidence to the contrary.*

honest look. They're afraid the bubble might burst; that they would see that they actually have a problem and are hurting themselves and maybe others. This could cause shame, embarrassment, or guilt. Worse still, they might feel as though they MUST cut back or quit using drugs; options that they don't even want to consider.

If drugs have been bringing you pleasure, helping you cope, and making you feel good, it's hard to consider making changes. It's hard to be clear-headed and open-minded about harm if you really like drugs a lot, or love them, or believe that you need them to feel good or to cope with life. Maybe, you really *don't* want to change. Perhaps you feel that you couldn't succeed in changing. Fear of failure sometimes keeps people from admitting to problems and even attempting to change. ("If I don't try, then I can't fail.")

To move forward, however, somehow you have to face reality, even if you don't like what you see. You have to believe in yourself and believe that if things aren't going right, you can make them better.

This book says: "If you want to change, you can do it." Plus, you can do it at your own pace, in your own way – building yourself up as you go along.

Furthermore, as much as you might miss drugs if you were to cut back or quit, there are other ways to cope, feel good, and meet your needs. You can master them.

As the King and Mathemagician said in *The Phantom Tollbooth*: "...so many things are possible just as long as you don't know they're impossible."[3]

HONEST WITH YOURSELF: THE CHALLENGING VOICE

Take a look around. You don't have to be a rocket scientist to know that people don't always make the best decisions in day-to-day living. They don't always do what's best for themselves.

Taking charge of your own life is a big challenge. It requires self-awareness – you've got to pay attention and know yourself. You

---

[3] *A wonderful book by Norton Juster.*

must intensely scrutinize your life, probe deeply, and look for the naked truth, whatever it may be – problems or not. And when you find problems and decide to make changes, you have to hold yourself accountable to your goals.

If you're not leaving it to other people to oversee your life, then you have to watch yourself. If no one is challenging you, then you have to challenge yourself. This requires brutal honesty and piercing self-awareness of what you're doing, why you're doing it, and the effects of your actions. Beware of self-deception: People tend to lie to themselves. Beware of complacency: People tend to keep doing what they have already been doing. Beware of making excuses: People tend to excuse things that shouldn't be excused. To succeed, there can be no complacency, no excuses, and no self-deception.

If you say "I know what I'm doing" without even pausing to reflect, then probably you do not. You shouldn't *start* with certainty. You need an open mind. First, you should carefully consider all the facts.

Most people don't *really* challenge themselves to look at the naked truth about their lives, though they may argue that they do. If they did really challenge themselves, we would have a lot fewer drug problems (and less obesity, less gambling, less debt, etc., etc.).

If you want to gain mastery of your life, you need to seek the facts and face the truth with a firm, challenging attitude. A practical and helpful way to do this is to think about having a voice within yourself that asks tough questions and reveals everything, even shortcomings and uncomfortable truths. The type of voice or "self-talk" that pushes you to succeed can be called the Challenging Voice.

From what I've said so far, I wouldn't blame you for thinking, "Yeah, right, just what I need. A critical person looking over my shoulder, picking me apart, and telling me everything I'm doing is wrong." So, I want to clarify: The Challenging Voice is actually on your side. It is supporting you in recognizing problems, making informed decisions about your life, clarifying your goals, staying focused on them, and persisting with your efforts so that you will succeed. It's not out to catch you doing wrong. It's out to help you notice when you have lost focus or gone off course, so that you can refocus, correct your course and attain your own goals, whatever they may be. It challenges you to examine your life and do everything it takes – to pull out all the stops – so that you can succeed.

THE CHALLENGING VOICE ABOUT DRUGS

If identifying drug problems and overcoming them were a simple matter, you wouldn't be reading this book. Truth is, it's a huge challenge. People find it hard to go beyond a superficial understanding of why they use drugs. They find it hard to admit to drug problems and the extent of the problems. When they do acknowledge problems, they find it hard to cut back or quit: they don't want to give up the benefits – the pleasure and relief that drugs provide.

The Challenging Voice doesn't relent. It insists that you look at the benefits you've been getting from drugs – the ways they have helped you cope. This often exposes personal weaknesses, shortcomings, underlying problems, and vulnerabilities. For example, you may discover that you have been using drugs to deal with insecurities about yourself, or with an inability to cope with various emotions, or moods, or the pain of trauma from the past.

The Challenging Voice also insists that you admit to the all harm that drugs have caused you; could cause you; and will cause you (if you keep going in the direction you're headed).

The Challenging Voice will not let you confuse a *desire* to stop the harm from drugs with something different; a *commitment* to actually making changes. If you contemplate quitting or setting new limits, it will ask:

- Are you *really* willing to make sacrifices and give up the drug benefits – the good stuff?
- Are you *really* willing to invest the extraordinary effort it will take to make changes…and stick with it?
- Do you *really* have confidence in your own ability to make changes? (If not, you're not likely to even try. So, increasing your self-confidence would have to be part of an effort to change your drug use behavior.)

If you do commit to change, the Challenging Voice wants to

know if you *will* really hold yourself accountable and *won't* make excuses when you lapse or relapse, or have other setbacks.

In short, the Challenging Voice demands honesty. It checks to see if you mean business. When it detects resistance or reluctance, it's your sign to "double up" on effort or get help, or else recognize that you're not ready to move forward.

CHALLENGING YOURSELF WITH TOUGH QUESTIONS ABOUT HARM FROM DRUGS

The Challenging Voice is not judgmental. It does not assume that you have drug problems. Rather, it challenges you to make your own call about this. It asks challenging questions and says: "No excuses and no rationalization." It insists that you think honestly about questions such as these:

- Am I harming my body?
- Am I harming my mind?
- Am I getting in trouble at work and/or school?
- Am I harming my family?
- Am I harming my romantic relationships/marriage?
- Am I harming my friendships?
- Am I harming other people?
- Am I harming my financial standing?
- Am I harming my reputation?
- Am I limiting my possibilities for the future?
- Am I giving up on my dreams?
- Are drugs interfering with career plans?
- Do I go to excess?
- Do I embarrass myself?
- Do I do crazy things that get me in trouble?
- Am I doing dangerous things?
- Is my drug use under control right now, or is it actually out of control?
- Am I always saying that things will get better in the future, but nothing has changed?
- Is my drug use causing legal consequences?
- Is there harm that could happen, but hasn't happened yet (for example from driving under the influence, or sex under the influence, or loosening up and doing things that are illegal or things that might be regretted later)?
- Am I headed toward harm in the future? What harm is likely

to occur if I keep going in the direction I am headed with alcohol and other drugs?

If there is harm or potential harm, then the Challenging Voice wants you to know the extent of it.

CHALLENGING YOURSELF WITH TOUGH QUESTIONS ABOUT DRUG BENEFITS

People often make 'harm-based decisions' to quit or cut back on their drug use. They want the harm to go away. They make this decision without realizing what it means – that they'll also lose the benefits from drugs. Unaware of what they're losing, they can't properly prepare for life after they quit or cut back. It's a naïve, "half-baked" decision to change – a set-up for failure.

The Challenging Voice insists that you look at the drug benefits – the good things you get from drugs. You have to dig inside yourself to discover your reasons for using – often this means admitting to underlying problems and shortcomings. People say they use drugs because they "like them" or they "feel good" or "it's a social thing," but as they dig deeper they may reveal personal vulnerabilities and find inconvenient and discomforting realities. For example, some people find that they use drugs to hold back painful feelings from past experiences, sometimes even pain from trauma. Some people discover that they have been masking very sad feelings or great anxiety. They are desperate and want to feel "nothing"... as much as possible. Some people find that they use drugs to cope with unhappiness from feeling trapped in bad relationships or marriages. Some people discover they use drugs because they are bored with life. The Challenging Voice begins to expose hidden pain, sadness, dissatisfaction, personal weakness, and various deficits.

To gain mastery over drugs, you can't cover your ears, hide your head in the sand, and ignore discomforting information.

CHALLENGING YOURSELF WITH TOUGH QUESTIONS ABOUT MAKING SACRIFICES

To make an informed decision about drugs, you have to think about what you will be giving up or losing if you cut back or quit – and then consider the new reality. Make no mistake: When you change your drug use behavior, you are making a sacrifice. You will be giving up the stuff you have liked about drugs.

- Maybe you used drugs to relax when you were tense or stressed. It'll go away. Gone!
- Maybe you used to fall asleep at night. Gone!
- Maybe to calm yourself down when you were angry. Gone!
- Maybe to feel comfortable in social situations. Gone!
- Maybe to block feelings of sadness or forget painful experiences. Gone!
- Maybe for fun, excitement, celebration, adventure, and overall good feelings. Gone!
- Maybe to alter your consciousness. Gone!
- Maybe you used because it was "what you do." It was your way of life. Gone!

Plus: If you reached the level of addiction, and you used drugs to avoid the psychological and physical pain of withdrawal. Gone!

The Challenging Voice probes deeply and asks, "Are you really ready for this?" It challenges you to think seriously about your life without drugs (or with less of them). You won't be able to fall back on your old and familiar ways of coping or finding pleasure.

When you think about what you will lose, you quickly realize that you can't make decisions about drugs without considering everything else that is going on in your life that is closely connected to your drug use. Yes, willpower is important. But how will you cope without drug benefits? How will you meet the needs that drugs were satisfying, or learn to live without these needs being met?

Clearly, there's much more to changing drug use behavior than simply saying NO. In later chapters you'll see clearly the connection between drug use and the rest of your life, and ideas about making positive changes in both realms.

SELF-TALK

When we look at what's happening in our lives, we are very much influenced by what goes on in our minds. You could say that we filter reality through our own personal lens. A helpful way to understand this thinking is by putting it into sentences; almost as if we were talking to ourselves – sort of an audio soundtrack that we play in our heads. This is called "self-talk." It has a huge influence on the quality of our lives and how we conduct ourselves. Broadly speaking, self-talk can be divided into two categories: Nurturing and Oppressive. Nurturing Self-talk is kind, supportive, understanding, and uplifting. Oppressive Self-talk is harsh, judgmental, and degrading. We all have some of each.

Nurturing Self-talk builds you up, and allows you to see your best qualities and feel good about yourself. It helps you feel strong so you can strive for mastery in your life. It says: "You can do it." When you make mistakes, it has compassion and helps you learn from them. It is reassuring and says: "Mistakes happen, let's figure this out." However, Nurturing Self-talk is not all warm and fuzzy. When things aren't going well, it speaks with a Challenging Voice (which has been discussed in earlier pages) that firmly pushes you to make decisions to change and do the hard work required to succeed with them. To be clear: The Challenging Voice is a type of Nurturing Self-talk. Because Nurturing Self-talk is based on a belief in your basic good nature and competency, it challenges you to make your life better.

In contrast, Oppressive Self-talk undermines you and puts you down. It judges and harshly criticizes. It makes you feel bad about yourself and powerless about making changes, with statements such as these:

"You're stupid. You're lazy. You're a loser. You're weak. You're to blame for everything. There's nothing you can do to change things."

When you make mistakes or suffer setbacks, Oppressive Self-talk goes on the attack, as in "You can't do it. You're a failure." With this sort of negativity, who would even admit to a problem? The result would surely be an attack from within…and feelings of guilt, shame, and powerlessness. Opressive Self-talk prevents people from making their lives better.

All of us have a combination of nurturing and oppressive thoughts in our minds. If you pay attention, you can "listen" to your self-talk and hear what it says. You can also change it – and change it for the better. That's part of gaining mastery over your life.

One of the goals of this book is to support you in strengthening and expanding your Nurturing Self-talk, and fighting and diminishing the Oppressive Self-talk. It'll help you make and succeed with drug decisions, and enhance every other aspect of your life.

OPPRESSIVE SELF-TALK ABOUT DRUGS

When it comes to drugs, Oppressive Self-talk is always ready to pounce. If you admit to problems, it'll judge you, blame you, call you weak-willed, and put you down with labels such as "druggie," "loser," or "addict." It's nasty. It'll tell you that you could never successfully cut back or quit. This type of self talk makes it exceedingly hard to admit to any drug issues whatsoever.

Furthermore, Oppressive Self-talk keeps you isolated.

"You made your bed, now sleep in it. Stand on your own two feet."

And if you want support, it protests: "Asking for help makes you look weak."

These pronouncements may sound like the truth, but really they represent a set of values – values that promote shame and a very lonely view of the world. Why must we stand alone? Problems didn't occur in a vacuum, isolated from other people, and need not be solved in that manner. On the contrary, we should seek and accept all the help that we can get.

Self-talk is learned. To a large extent, what you say to yourself is influenced by what you have heard from others. When people have been critical and judgmental of you, you internalize that. When people have doubted your character or abilities, you tend to believe them. Fortunately, Oppressive Self-talk can be challenged, unlearned, and replaced with Nurturing Self-talk.

NURTURING SELF-TALK ABOUT DRUGS

Nurturing Self-talk is about looking at yourself in the best possible way. It builds you up and supports you. It approves of you (faults, warts, and all), encourages you, and is on your side in helping you learn from all your experiences.

The message of Nurturing Self-talk is: "I'm fine. I'm strong. I can do it."

This talk recognizes your strengths and the good things about you. It's not delusional and grandiose – pumping you up with ridiculous claims. Rather it allows you to see the good qualities that you truly possess. If you don't give yourself credit for the good things about yourself, it will be much harder to accept the problems. It will also be hard to fight off the Oppressive Self-talk that puts you down.

Unfortunately, many people have trouble recognizing their good qualities and standing up for themselves. If you have this difficulty, then it's an issue that will be important to address. This book offers help in developing Nurturing Self-talk and in challenging Oppressive Self-talk. Also, as you work to improve your life, your positive feelings about yourself will slowly but surely increase.

You might think that Nurturing Self-talk would gloss over anything negative. This is definitely not the case. Nurturing Self-talk must be realistic. It accepts and recognizes problems, shortcomings, setbacks, and mistakes – including about the use of drugs. These are not fatal flaws. They are simply part of life; experiences that provide us with an opportunity to learn, develop, and change for the better. Nurturing Self-talk is a compassionate way to understand how life problems have occurred and what we can do to improve things. People who don't learn from problems and setbacks get stuck in a rut.

Even if you are addicted to drugs, Nurturing Self-talk won't label you "an addict." Your identity is not defined by your drug use. Instead, it would say you are "a person with a serious drug problem," or "a person with a drug addiction." As the Nurturing Self-talk gets stronger, it would say you're "a *good person* who has a serious problem with drugs."

Nurturing Self-talk also means coming to believe in your own personal power. That is: If you set your mind to accomplish something, work hard, and get the right type of support, then you can succeed in most anything you do, including efforts to overcome drug problems.

FEEDBACK FROM OTHERS

As you ask yourself challenging questions and evaluate your life, it's important to remember that we humans see things from our own point of view and are not always the most objective and honest judges of ourselves. Too often we make excuses, distort reality, and even lie to ourselves. Sometimes other people can see things about us that we, ourselves, cannot see or did not notice or chose to overlook. That's why we can benefit from the feedback of others – honest insight, including constructive criticism given from a caring perspective to build us up, rather than tear us down. It makes sense to seek out and listen to this feedback. It allows us to overcome blind spots and increase self-understanding. It's like a coach helping an athlete; a teacher helping a student; and a friend helping a friend.

Although some people are very supportive in sharing their perspective, others are hurtful and can be terribly judgmental and harshly critical. If you've been judged harshly and negatively in the past, you might be tempted to put up a wall. You also might react defensively to helpful feedback. So, when someone offers constructive criticism or other supportive feedback, you would "hear" negative judgments when none were intended.

If you push people away, you won't get hurt. However, you also won't get valuable information. In searching for the naked truth about yourself, it's essential to be receptive to what *supportive people* have to say. This means opening yourself up. The difficult challenge is to ignore or reject harsh judgments and put downs, while seeking and paying attention to the important constructive feedback that may be available. This feedback helps you see yourself as you really are – including flaws and problems.

SELF-HELP OR COUNSELING?

This self-help book is written to support you in thinking about your own life and your use of alcohol and other drugs. At a minimum, I'm hoping you'll find inspiration and helpful suggestions. If you have a serious drug problem, I'm hoping you'll do the hard work of reading this book carefully and putting the information to work in taking control of your life. Even though it is self-help, if you want to make changes, you shouldn't have to do it alone. It's your choice, but most people benefit from getting support.

Many people who have drug problems eventually get better on their own, without the benefit of any sort of support group or counseling services. You could say that they "mature out" of their drug problems. The problem with this, however, is that not all people mature out of them, and significant damage can occur before they do. That's why I highly recommend getting the support of people who care about you and are willing to be honest and supportive. I especially recommend using counselors who believe in you and your personal power, and are skilled in promoting both honest self-appraisal and determined efforts to change. You deserve all the support you can get.

CHALLENGE ONE: SUMMARY AND ACTION STEPS

This book is written to support you in making your own thoughtful decisions about your life, including your drug use. I'm not pushing an agenda. Because no one should be looking over your shoulder (and if they are – it's still your life, not theirs), you are responsible for your own thoughtful decisions. The burden falls on you. And that's a good thing. Embrace it.

At this point, the key actions you can take will really test your readiness to succeed:

1) Can you be ruthlessly honest in looking at yourself and your actions? Can you look in the mirror and see what is there – no distortions, no excuses? Can you admit to problems and mistakes?

2) When it comes to drugs, see if you can muster up a Challenging Voice that wants to know the naked truth about your drug use – why you use, how much, how often, how it benefits you, how it harms you, and where you seem to be headed.

3) See if you can honestly answer all the questions about how drugs may have harmed you in any aspect of your life. See page 18 (Challenging Yourself with Tough Questions about Harm from Drugs).

4) See if you can identify which of your own shortcomings your drug use may be masking. See page 19 (Challenging Yourself with Tough Questions about Drug Benefits).

Be brave and tell all the details of your drug use to at least one person you trust. Ask this person for feedback about your drug use.

At this time, do you want to set limits or quit your use of alcohol or other drugs, either because you are under pressure from a family member or someone else, or because of the level of your own concern? If so, start reading Challenge Seven on page 115, and then return back to Challenge Two and continue reading the whole book.

Start applying the Mastery Approach to Life. Start to identify what is not going well, or as well as you would like it to be going, in your life. These are your issues. (No one has a perfect life – we all have issues.) Write some of them down. On your own, or with the help of others (including a counselor if you wish), begin to work on your issues, one-by-one.

Pay attention and learn to recognize your self-talk.

Think about how Nurturing Self-talk supports you in facing personal problems. Start to write the words for your own Nurturing Self-talk.

Identify and write down the words of your Oppressive Self-talk.

Begin to think of powerful answers to Oppressive Self-talk. Write them down.

Remind yourself of the option of talking openly to a counselor for help with any personal matter. You don't have to do everything alone. This book is educational in nature and should not be considered a substitute for mental health or drug counseling.

CHALLENGE TWO

Challenging yourself to look at
what you like about alcohol and other drugs
and why you use them

THE GOOD STUFF ABOUT DRUGS

When you first tried drugs, you were probably curious about them – wondering what they would do for you. If you kept using them, it meant you found something you liked. That's precisely why people use drugs. They like the effects.

Challenge Two is about what you have liked about drugs: drug benefits. With this challenge, you get a chance to think in great detail about the good stuff: the pleasures you have derived and the needs you have satisfied or attempted to satisfy by using them. This is important information; important for decision-making and equally important for people who want to change their drug use behavior.

If you want to make informed decisions about drugs, then half of the equation is knowing the benefits you would be losing if you were to quit or set new limits. You need this information to fully understand all the implications of such a decision: how your life would be different without drugs or with less drugs.

If you've already decided to set new limits or quit, then you need to know the drug benefits you have forsaken. This knowledge allows you to search for other ways to satisfy your needs and/or to prepare for life without these needs being satisfied. It's the key to long-term success in overcoming drug problems: Willpower in resisting drugs will only take you so far. Beyond that, you need to figure out how to have a good life without drugs or with less of them.

If you've previously made decisions to cut back or quit but had trouble adhering to them, then you need to know which drug benefits were compelling enough to have overridden your desire to change. Therefore, knowledge of what you have liked about drugs is hugely important. With that knowledge you can begin to find other ways to cope with life, without needing to rely on drugs. You can reaffirm your decision to change and be better prepared to resist urges to use drugs in the future.

WINDOW TO SELF UNDERSTANDING

Sometimes people know exactly why they are using drugs. For example, someone may be aware of feeling tense at the end of the day and decide to drink to deliberately reduce the tension.

Someone may be feeling some sort of emotional pain and then use a drug to numb the pain and forget what is causing it.

Someone may be bored and decide to get high to have some fun.

Quite often, however, people don't pinpoint their reasons for using. They don't think much about the details. They just know that drugs "feel good." Or, they explain their drug use by saying: "It's just what I do." They're not aware of anything more specific than that.

If you want to make wise and informed decisions about drugs, you have to dig deeper and get the whole picture. You have to understand your specific reasons for using them.

Questions such as these help you get the big picture:

- What do I specifically like about using drugs?
- What is it about each drug that I like?
- What thoughts, feelings, or situations make me want to use?
- What do I want to have happen when I use?

Answering these questions will help you understand your reasons for using drugs. Some people can easily pinpoint their reasons. Others have to work hard to pin them down. Some people find one main reason, while others find a variety of them. Sometimes, it's like peeling an onion. You identify some of the more obvious reasons for drug use at first, but have to look deep inside to uncover more hidden motives. In this chapter, you'll find lists of reasons why people use drugs and many examples. You can use these lists and examples to try to clarify your own reasons.

DRUG OF CHOICE; CHOICE OF DRUGS

People respond differently to drugs and have different preferences, or drugs of choice. One person may drink alcohol to relax and sleep, while another drinks to cut loose at a party. It is very individual.

Sometimes people use different drugs to experience different feelings. For example, a person might use a prescription medication such as Oxycontin® to relax; cocaine for a rush of energy; and alcohol to release inhibitions at a party.

HIDDEN REASONS

As I previously noted, when people are asked what they like about drugs, many of them reply: "They make me feel good." That's a broad, sweeping statement that explains very little and can have very different meanings. If you want to better understand yourself and your own reasons for using drugs, it's important to dig deeper.

What do you really like about drugs? What is it that feels good?

- Some people feel good because they stop feeling sad.
- Some people feel good because they stop feeling angry or hurt.
- Some people feel good because they are brave and readily do things they would never do sober.
- Some people feel good because they stop being bored.

Here are some more reasons people use drugs:

- To calm down when they are tense
- To have fun
- To fall asleep
- To get wasted and not feel anything
- To relieve pressure from work
- To stop feeling miserable about a job
- To escape from feeling miserable about a spouse/romantic partner
- To forget troubles
- To stop unpleasant thoughts
- To improve their mood
- To feel energetic
- To feel happy
- To celebrate
- To reduce stress
- To control anger
- To feel comfortable with friends
- To annoy someone who wants them to abstain
- To "fit in" or be liked
- To get away with something
- To loosen up and talk on dates or at parties or at other social engagements
- To tolerate bad situations
- To numb themselves

- To show off
- For excitement: to live on the edge and be crazy

ASKING ONE MORE QUESTION

To gain greater self-understanding about yourself and your reasons for using drugs, it often helps to "ask one more question." As you know, drug use has a lot to do about everything else in your life (besides drugs).

- When you use drugs to forget problems, which problems?
- When you use your drugs to take your mind off things, what things?
- When you use drugs to relax, what causes you to feel tense?
- When you use drugs to calm down, why are you worked up?
- When you use drugs to ease the pressure, what pressure are you feeling?
- When you use drugs to control your anger, why are you angry?

Your answers to questions of this sort help you better understand where drugs fit in your life.

ASKING STILL MORE QUESTIONS

If you start by asking yourself "what do I like about drugs" or "when do I feel like using drugs" and then keep asking yourself a series of questions, you can more fully understand your motivation for using drugs and gain insight into important issues in your life.

Here is an example, showing a Question and Answer dialogue:

Q: When do I like to get high?
A: Before going to bed.
Q: What do I like about getting high before I go to bed?
A: It lets me sleep.
Q: What happens if I don't get high before bedtime?
A: I can't sleep. I worry. My mind races wild.
(This would be an example of someone using drugs to deal with anxiety and a sleep problem.)

Questioning could continue by asking: "What do I worry about?" Through this type of a questioning process, you can gain clarity about your situation and uncover the underlying reasons for drug use.

Here is a second example.

Q: When do I like to get high?
A: I like to get high when I'm angry.
Q: What do I like about getting high when I'm angry?
A: It calms me down and I don't do anything I regret.
Q: What happens if I don't get high?
A: Sometimes I blow up and do something stupid.
(This would be an example of using drugs to manage anger.)

Questioning could continue by asking: "What sort of situations make me angry?"

PROBLEMS IN YOUR LIFE

When you look at your reasons for using drugs over a period of time, certain patterns appear. You gradually uncover the conditions and situations that "trigger" your use.

It could be in response to feelings about long-standing and enduring problems (such as problems with romantic relationships; family issues; work related matters; financial stress; an unhappy social life).

It could be in response to specific types of situations (such as when you're upset by an argument; angry about something; criticized by someone; in conflict with authority).

It could be in response to certain moods and negative feelings (such as anger, emotional pain, sadness, or depression).

It could be when you are bored and wanting to have fun, or seeking excitement. Or, when you want to socialize with friends. Or, when you feel stressed.

As you learn your triggers for drug use, you get to know yourself better and may discover underlying problems. Here are some examples:

- If you use drugs to "self-medicate" sad feelings, you may find that you are often unhappy and depressed.
- If you often use drugs to calm yourself when worried, you may find that you have an anxiety problem.

- If you often use drugs to have fun, you may find that you are bored and have difficulty creating a fun and exciting recreational life for yourself.
- If you often use drugs to stop thinking about things that feel bad, you may find that you have specific problems in your life that need to be addressed, or possibly tragic or traumatic memories that you try to forget.

This isn't to say that everyone has deep, underlying issues. However, people who use drugs to excess often discover that there are other important problems behind their drug problems.

Whether you decide to keep using drugs or not, the identification of drug triggers provides you with an opportunity to consider other ways – besides drugs – to deal with issues in your life.

MORE OPTIONS

Once you know why you use drugs and how you have used them to meet particular needs, you then have the option of finding new ways to satisfy these needs. You also could learn to tolerate feelings that you have previously "medicated away" with drugs. Here are a few examples.

- If you used drugs to deal with anxiety before bed, you could instead figure out what was making you anxious and make plans to deal with the problems. Or, you could learn other ways to calm yourself down when feeling anxious, such as with relaxation skills, deep breathing, or various stress reduction strategies. You also could get help learning skills to counter sleep disorders. There are many very practical solutions for sleep problems.
- If you used drugs to calm your anger, you could instead use other options, such as trying to resolve the issue(s) that caused the anger or learning different ways to tolerate or manage the feeling.
- If you used drugs to "medicate" disappointment, you could instead decide to tolerate the feeling for a while, knowing that it would pass in time and when it does, you could move forward in any way you choose.

Knowing what drives your drug use gives you the option of finding other ways to deal with life. It does not mean you *have to* find other ways. However, it is almost always beneficial to solve problems that can be solved and to expand your own coping mechanisms, regardless of what you decide to do about drugs.

DRUGS WITH FRIENDS

Though many people use drugs alone, often they do it as part of a social life, either with one friend or a group of friends. Do you use drugs socially? Drugs can serve various functions:

- As a social ritual – a way to hang out and structure time with friends. It's "what you do" when you get together.
- As a way to relax and feel comfortable with friends.
- As a way to release inhibitions – to really cut loose and talk, or dance, or get wild.
- As a way to calm anxiety and avoid appearing to be socially awkward in tense social situations, such as at parties or when meeting a potential new friend or dating partner.

Sometimes people even build their social identity around their alcohol or drug use. They get known as a heavy hitter, or a big drinker, or someone who loves to "party." College students and other young adults often go on alcohol or drug binges as part of their social life.

CHANGING FEELINGS

As you think about what you like about drugs, bear in mind that people often use drugs to change how they feel.

Drugs can calm a worried mind; comfort a sad mind; excite a bored mind; cool down an angry mind; ease a pained mind. They provide an escape from the various emotions that go with the problems of daily living.

Drugs can lift your mood. Some of them numb negative feelings such as sadness and depression. Others actually override negative feelings with positive ones. Drugs can stimulate feelings of joyfulness, intoxication, or even ecstasy.

- A woman who was overcome with worries about her children, her elderly parents, and the family's financial situation started abusing prescription medications and drinking to calm herself down.
- A man who was nervous in social encounters of any sort used a whole array of drugs – whatever he had at the time – to relax when he was around people.

- A woman who just wanted to escape her pain, especially about the loss of custody of her children, blotted out her feelings with heroin.
- A man who resented that his girlfriend "called the shots" suppressed his anger with marijuana and the occasional use of alcohol.
- A young woman who had been sexually abused as a child drank during her teen years to deal with her pain. Later, she started using crack and meth.
- A guy in his twenties started drinking heavily in the military, mainly to socialize. Once discharged, he used heroin to deal with the pain and anguish of some of his wartime experiences.

Not only can drugs change feelings, but they also give a sense of power. They give you a very simple way to control what you feel. This can be extremely important if you are not aware of other ways to influence what you feel.

FEELINGS ABOUT YOURSELF

Sometimes people use drugs to stop bad feelings about themselves and to stop their own negative self-talk. They may feel bad about themselves because of problems in many realms of their lives – perhaps at work, in school, at home, in a loving relationship, with family, with friends, or with the law. They may feel bad about themselves because they have hurt other people, or because they are hurting themselves with self-destructive behavior. They might even feel bad about themselves because they have a drug problem, and then try to make those negative feelings go away by using more drugs.

People who put themselves down a lot will generally blame themselves for everything bad that happens; see themselves as worthless and powerless; and assume that other people think of them in an equally negative and critical way. As one woman who put herself down relentlessly said, she drank alcohol or used pills to "quiet her mind."

People lacking in self-confidence who want to feel brave or calm in certain social settings or tense work situations, sometimes use drugs to mask their insecurity. Drugs allow them to be braver than they would be otherwise.

One woman had very disapproving parents who fostered her low self-esteem. She spent her life trying to win love and approval. She married a man who never seemed to approve of her, sometimes treating her with disdain. She was always trying to please him. She had three children. Even as a middle-aged adult/parent she still kept trying to win the approval of her parents and husband. The only relief she found from her own sense of being "unlovable" was to escape by taking tranquilizers or drinking alcohol.

RELATIONSHIP PROBLEMS

Long-standing relationship problems with a spouse or romantic partner are a major trigger for drug use. Sometimes people feel bad about their relationships, don't see a way to fix them or have not been able to fix them, so they use drugs to escape. They may feel pain, hurt, and anger; and want to stop their minds from dwelling on the relationship.

- A man who feels that his partner is very controlling, sneaks off to do cocaine during the day. He feels good from the drugs and doubly good that his partner cannot control him in this domain.
- A widowed woman married a guy who she feels is emotionally cold and "never listens" to her. She drinks to escape her angry and pained feelings. When he "catches" her and gets angry, she feels free to retaliate by letting him know how disappointed she is in the relationship.
- A young man feels excessively pushed to achieve by his boyfriend. He uses a variety of drugs to "forget" his situation, to escape his presence, and hang out with friends. He secretly hopes that his partner will break up with him and end the relationship.

WORK SITUATION

Work and career problems of all sorts can trigger drug use. Here's a small sample of the situations that I've heard about in counseling:

- A woman who hates her job uses pills to numb herself at work.
- Angry about things at work and in particular about an incompetent and unfair boss, a married father comes home angry at the world. He smokes marijuana every day to chill

out. Sometimes when things are really bad on the job, he gets high at work.

- In his mid twenties now, a bright young man had been an underachiever in high school due to drug use and other emotional problems. He fell behind, works for minimum wage, and feels hopeless about any sort of career possibilities. He takes opioids regularly, and manipulates friends and family to pay for it.
- A very young mother who has been using drugs since high school feels hopeless about supporting herself and her child. For financial reasons, she gets involved with abusive guys who sell meth. She trades sex for drugs in order to keep going and have a place to crash.
- A man who has been driven to succeed in a career since childhood and now has a high paying job feels empty and burdened by pressure. He uses a variety of drugs to "blow his mind" and tolerate all the stress.

LET THE GOOD TIMES ROLL

Sometimes people simply seek pleasure and enjoyment from drugs. They're not trying to make bad feelings go away. Rather, they're looking to create good ones – happy times and euphoric experiences. Drugs make them laugh and just plain feel great. When they think of fun and good times, drugs immediately pop into their minds. When they think about celebrating a special occasion, alcohol or other drugs are always part of the picture.

To break the routine of a mundane life, some people use hallucinogens to alter their reality. Some people chase feelings; seeking the rush, thrill, and excitement they get from drugs.

For many young adults, partying means getting together to indulge. Alcohol and marijuana are often the drugs of choice, along with whatever else might be available. Ecstasy and various pills are featured at some social gatherings.

Alcohol, in particular, is often tied to the idea of "good times," whether it's at a bar, with a meal, or in front of a televised sports event.

It's not just a "kid" thing. For example, a guy in his mid-forties would leave his wife and children at home when he met with his male friends who used cocaine and alcohol to have a good time. They would get together and get rowdy until all hours of the night.

A group of elderly friends met regularly and drank heavily at what they humorously referred to as a "tea party."

When you think about what you like about drugs, don't forget that they may be helpful in the pursuit of pleasure.

ALL THE GOOD THINGS

To summarize, certain conditions, emotions, and specific situations make you want to use drugs. Drugs can help in various ways:

- They turn off your mind.
- They numb or change emotions.
- They counteract stress.
- They give you a way to control your behavior and keep you from behaving in unwanted ways.
- They provide escape – a way to avoid dealing with situations or conditions you do not want to face. You exit "straight" reality and enter your own world.
- They remove inhibition and give you courage to deal with difficult situations.
- They can counteract boredom.
- They can be a way to have fun and celebrate.

A TURNING POINT

If you think your drug use might have reached problematic levels, one way to more fully understand drug benefits is to think back to when your use began to escalate. What was going on in your life at that time? When you think back, you might link your escalating use to life circumstances – the problems and distress at a moment in time. Then, you can see how you turned to drugs to navigate those difficulties.

Clearly, people use drugs to find pleasure and relief from pain. However, it can be a risky venture. The more often they dip into the well, the greater the potential for problems. The risks, dangers, and harm from drug use are addressed in Challenge Three.

USING TO FEEL NORMAL

When people find something they really like about drugs, they may begin to use regularly to attain the desired effect – whether it's for pleasure or the reduction of pain. The problem with this is that their bodies develop "tolerance" to the effects. This means they need more and more drugs to attain the same good feeling. Then, more and more again. Eventually they get addicted. If they keep at it, the tolerance is so great that they can no longer attain the good feeling at all. But their brain still craves the drugs.

Once addicted, it's hard to stop. When they try to stop, they go through the negative experience called withdrawal. It's extremely uncomfortable and unpleasant, both physically and psychologically. With certain drugs it is medically dangerous.

One way to stop the craving and avoid the pain of withdrawal is to keep on using drugs. At this point, the use is no longer to feel good. It's to prevent negative feelings – i.e., the "crash" of withdrawal. This is called "using to feel normal."

If you have reached the level of drug addiction, you may not be aware of *attaining any of the benefits you used to get.* You are simply driven to use for a different reason: to either avoid the terrible discomfort and pain of withdrawal, or to provide relief from it.

CHALLENGE TWO: SUMMARY AND ACTION STEPS

People use drugs to satisfy personal needs. So, if you want to make informed decisions about drugs or change your drug use behavior, it's important to understand your own motivation. It's not always obvious. Sometimes you have to dig deep. Sometimes when you dig, you expose personal weaknesses or shortcomings that have been masked by drugs.

The first action step with Challenge Two is to identify and write down your reasons for using drugs. You can refer back to page 30 (Hidden Reasons) and page 38 (All The Good Things) for help in composing your list. As time passes, you may uncover more reasons and add them to this list. The issues revealed on pages 31 (Asking One More Question) and 31-32 (Asking Still More Questions) can help you with this.

As you identify what you have liked about drugs, you can begin to make sense of your reasons for using them. Write a paragraph that explains it all. Here's a suggestion about how to start.

"I can see why I use drugs. I use them because they benefit me in these ways: ……… "

Caution: Avoid the tendency to shift your focus to the harm from drugs. You'll get to that in the next challenge. At this point, it would interfere with the current (and important) task of making sense of your own motivation. You're not defending your drug use; just trying to understand it. This knowledge is an essential part of overcoming drug problems.

Next, review the list and paragraph you wrote. You'll see that you have used drugs to deal with certain uncomfortable feelings and problem situations. Regardless of your ultimate decisions about drugs, you can benefit from this information: It exposes problems you could solve to improve your life. Write down the problems you identify, and start working on one of them. You could pick the most pressing problem or the easiest one to solve. Which one do you choose? Do you want to work on it alone or with the help of a counselor or someone else you trust? Don't hesitate to get help from a counseling professional if you are distressed.

There's still more work to do. Review your list and paragraph again. This time do it with an eye toward expanding your array of skills. Compose a list of the skills that could improve the quality of your life. Here's a short list of possibilities that might help you: anger management, stress management, impulse control, deep breathing, progressive relaxation (of muscles), meditation, communication skills for work, communication skills for relationships, assertiveness, problem solving skills, the skill of planning a recreational life, sleep hygiene (to avoid insomnia). Now you can get to work on the skills on your list, either on your own or with help.

Knowledge of what motivates your drug use will provide a springboard to gaining greater mastery over your life. It will also be essential to your success if you ever decide to set new limits or quit using drugs. Don't minimize its importance in taking a leap of power.

SAVE YOUR LISTS AND PARAGRAPH. YOU'LL WANT TO REFER TO THEM LATER.

CHALLENGE THREE

Challenging yourself to look at harm
that has happened and could happen
from your use of alcohol and other drugs

NO RUBBING IT IN

Challenge Three is about the harm from drugs: important information for people who have already decided to quit or set new limits, and for people who are trying to make decisions about whether to change.

Readers who have already decided to make changes may think: "I know I've been harmed. No point rubbing it in." Agreed, no point rubbing it in. However, there is a very important benefit to *clearly comprehending the full extent of the harm.* This information helps you persevere in your efforts to change. Harping on harm doesn't convince people to change (it leads to defensiveness). However, paying attention to harm is how people who have *already decided to change* can stay motivated. They remind themselves frequently of why they are doing what they are doing. The Challenging Voice tells them to remember the harm and stick with their decision or else things can go south.

FINGER POINTING AND DEFENSIVENESS

Some people know, without doubt, that their drug use has been harmful. Some may even know they have an addiction issue. For everyone else, it's more complicated. With all the finger pointing, blaming, and moralizing that goes around, it's easy to get defensive about drugs. It's easy to brush off and ignore people who tell you that you've got a problem. When you defend yourself, guess what? It gets turned around. You get accused of being "in denial." Truth be told, much of what has been labeled as denial is really just a normal, defensive response to an onslaught of negative judgments. This onslaught makes it difficult to do something vitally important in making informed decisions about drugs: to *realistically and honestly* appraise the harm. Drugs can cause harm, sometimes serious and even life-threatening. So, if you use drugs, you have to rise above the natural tendency to get defensive.

When people start using drugs, no one expects it will turn into a problem. Many people use in safe ways. Trouble is, almost everyone thinks that they are in this category – the safe one – including those who are actually harming themselves. So, if you want to determine whether you've been harmed by drugs, you really need to challenge yourself and be ruthlessly honest. You'll have to fight the inclination to immediately proclaim, "Everything is OK," without even thinking about it. Maybe it really is OK, but you have to honestly check it out. One strategy for doing this is to take the opposite approach. That is, assume the possibility of problems, make yourself an imaginary detective,[4] and challenge yourself to find them. This chapter describes the various ways people can be harmed by drugs. Use it to gain clarity about the ways your drug use may have been harmful to you.

To make informed decisions, you need to know the truth. If you find that you have been harmed by drugs, it doesn't mean that you *must* change. You still have choices. Maybe what you like about drugs is worth the price you pay: you take the bad with the good. OR, maybe it's time for a change. That's for you to decide.

NO SHAME AND NO PANIC

In addition to a critical and judgmental public – and maybe because of it – people often feel embarrassed and ashamed of having drug problems. To avoid a blow to their self-esteem, many of them deny problems that actually exist. They don't even want to think about it. They say, "I don't care," or brush off concerns with a glib, "I could stop whenever I want." But that's just phony nurturing – jumping to reassuring thoughts without even considering the facts.

If you find yourself *very eager* to say, "I don't care," then probably it means you were wondering whether you should care. If you were *very intent* on saying, "I could stop whenever I want," then probably you were wondering if you could stop. Instead of phony nurturing, you need a Challenging Voice that insists you look for the truth. When you know the truth, whatever it is, you can act on it. The Challenging Voice allows you to see if your drug use has caused harm. After all, everyone has problems in life. The challenge is to admit to problems without shame and then, most importantly, solve them. The goal with an honest and nurturing self-evaluation is to see the truth so you can make the best possible life for yourself.

Be honest with yourself: If your drug use is causing harm, it is in your best interest to know it. No need to panic. You can do something about it. Time and time again, people take power over their lives and solve problems; whether it's a problem with drugs or anything else.

---

[4] *Frank Schwebel suggested the concept of an imaginary detective.*

ONLY WHEN I FEEL LIKE IT

Sometimes people say, "I don't have a problem. I only drink (or do drugs) when I feel like it." They think that this proves something. But when you really think about that, anyone could say it. They just drink or do drugs when they *feel* like it. Why would they do otherwise? What else would they do? Would they use drugs when they don't feel like it? That makes no sense.

Some simple questions you can ask yourself to uncover the possibility of harm include the following:

- When do you feel like it?
- How often do you feel like it?
- How often do you use?
- How much do you use?
- What happens when you use?
- Do you have control right now?
- Could you really cut back or quit if you wanted to do that?
- Have you ever tried? If so, how did it go?

IF I'M NOT CRAVING DRUGS, I'M FINE

When thinking about drug problems, some people only think about extremes, such as addiction. From their point of view, problems don't begin until you crave drugs constantly and your life revolves around them: when you'll do anything and give up everything to obtain them; when you'll sell your possessions, steal cars, or trade sex for drugs.

Then, they compare themselves to the extremes. I don't have a problem because…

"I'm not living in the park and drinking liquor out of a paper bag."
"I don't have track marks all over my body."
"I don't drink or use drugs every day. I can stop."

By comparing themselves to others, people avoid taking a hard look at themselves. By using this standard, they can say "No problems yet," even when substantial harm has already occurred. (It's kind of like the wife who says, "My marriage is good because my husband doesn't beat me.") This thinking could be called: "It's not a problem until it's a disaster."

Furthermore, you don't have to be addicted to have problems

associated with drug use. An enormous amount of harm happens to people who are not addicted. Also, contrary to the myths, addiction doesn't spring up overnight. People have drug preferences and may find one particular drug to be especially appealing. They may use it a lot and come back for more. But it takes time for addiction to develop. So, if you see yourself increasingly drawn to a drug and using more and more of it to get the same effect, don't fall in the trap of comparing yourself to someone fully addicted. You should recognize the harm that may have already occurred or could occur, and be aware of the risk of things getting worse.

SOME BASIC QUESTIONS

The Challenging Voice doesn't assume you have a drug problem, but it wants you to know the truth. If you are convinced you have a problem, the questions below give you a chance to consider the harm that has occurred. If you're not sure about having a problem, they will help you reflect upon the possibility. Later you can determine what, if anything, you want to do about it.

Start with basics.

- Have you made serious mistakes under the influence?
- Have you embarrassed yourself?
- Have you failed to fulfill responsibilities?
- Have you avoided situations you should have confronted?
- Have you performed subpar or poorly at work (or in school)?
- Have you hurt your family or other people who love you?
- Have you damaged your relationship with friends or co-workers?
- Have you misbehaved under the influence?
- Have you gotten in trouble for your drug use (legal or otherwise)?
- Have you used at high levels and/or a frequency that has or could harm your mind or your body?
- Have you compromised your own values under the influence?
- Have you spent too much money on alcohol or other drugs?

Sometimes it helps to go by categories. Has your drug use harmed…

- Your health
- Your career (work life and/or school)
- Your love life/marriage
- Your family relationships

- Your parenting
- Your friendships
- Your reputation
- Your sense of self-esteem
- Your financial status
- Your pursuit of life goals/dreams

Any "yes" answer to these questions should trigger additional probing on your part to get at the specifics and to assess the seriousness of the harm.

IT COULD HAPPEN

In thinking about harmful drug use, don't overlook "high-risk behavior." That is, things that people sometimes do when using drugs, such as driving under the influence, having sex under the influence, or seeking certain types of thrills under the influence. You may or may not have been hurt by this. Maybe you drove under the influence without getting a DUI or hurting yourself or anyone else. Maybe you had unprotected sex and there was no unwanted pregnancy and no sexually transmitted infection. Maybe you have been lucky so far, but how long will your luck hold out? In making decisions about your drug use, it's important to consider risks – harm that could occur.

Consuming very large amounts of alcohol or other drugs, also known as bingeing, poses a special risk of harm. Bad things can happen when people are wasted or semi-incapacitated. Not every time, but the risk is always there. They can lose self-control and do things they regret. They may pass out, find themselves in an unexpected setting (a bathroom, someone's living room, in bed with a stranger, in jail, in an emergency room), and not even remember what happened.

Some people use drugs most of the time in moderation but occasionally binge or get totally wasted. This pattern can be a big problem.

HARMFUL DRUG USE

Drug use can be categorized in terms of levels. It begins as *experimentation* and then can progress to *occasional use* when opportunities present themselves. Next comes *regular use*, when people begin to look for drugs if they are not immediately available. They're seeking pleasure or relief from pain, or both. If they really like drugs and don't have other good options for feeling good or reducing pain, they may keep coming back for more and more. The more they use, the more likely that some sort of *harmful use* could occur. One problem with frequent drug use is that the body accommodates to the chemicals. It develops *"tolerance"* to them and needs ever-increasing amounts to attain the same effect. So drug use can increase further, leading to the highest level, which is called *addiction*.

Occasional use and even a single episode of use can cause harm with people doing stupid, crazy, irresponsible, embarrassing, or dangerous things. Under the influence people sometimes have motor vehicle crashes, unwanted sex, get pregnant, or make someone pregnant. They have fights, commit crimes, and get arrested. One such event can be life changing. Furthermore, people sometimes overdose. Overdoses of opioids[5] and other drugs, as well as dangerous drug combinations such as combining two depressants (for example, Valium and alcohol)[6] can cause serious health consequences, including death.

Ongoing drug use, even in moderation, can eat away at a person's well-being; causing problems on the job or in a family. Like the person whose drug use leads to absenteeism from work and poor job performance while under the influence. Like the husband upset about his family life who escapes from his problems with secretive drug use, gradually withdrawing from his spouse and failing to care for his children. Although health consequences can occur at any level of drug use, the risk increases as use escalates.

---

[5]*Everyone who uses opioids should know how to access Naloxone, a life-saving medication when there has been an overdose. Information can be found at https://addiction.surgeongeneral.gov/chapter-4-treatment.pdf*

[6]*Depressant drugs combine "synergistically," which means that together the effect of two different depressants is more than the sum of its parts. It is kind of like 1+1=3. Coma or death can result from these dangerous drug combinations.*

THE PROBLEMS WITH ESCAPING REALITY

Drugs can provide a temporary "vacation" or escape from reality. They offer a way to step back and forget troubles, not feel what you are feeling, and not think about something that is upsetting. They can numb and relax you. They give you a sense that you're in control of your emotions. However, too much of a good thing can spell trouble. If you use drugs as the only way or main way to cope with life, you may be allowing problems to persist that should be addressed. You dodge problems, but miss opportunities to possibly solve them. Sooner or later they catch up with you. Often they get worse. Then, of course, you want even more drugs to feel OK.

Another consequence of dodging problems is a different type of harm – a type that can be understood by what did **not** happen that should have happened. During the time that people are using drugs to escape, there are things they could or should be doing – such as learning how to cope with life's difficulties in different ways; learning how to solve problems; and learning new life skills. Instead, they drift through life and miss important opportunities for personal growth. Hard to recognize, this type of harm sneaks up on them later, when problems get serious and their toolbox for coping is practically empty.

- A woman in her late twenties drank alcohol to escape from conflict and her bad feelings about her spouse. She and her spouse still fight about almost everything, Now it's about her drinking, too. Worse still, on several occasions she has picked up their children at school and driven home while under the influence of alcohol.

A lot of drug use begins and escalates during adolescence and young adulthood when individuals should be learning life skills and new coping mechanisms.

- Looking back at his adolescence, a 30-year-old man talked about not wanting to seem "stupid" around his friends. He figured that if he was high all the time, people would think it was the drugs, not him, that made him stupid. That was fifteen years ago. Now an adult, he never learned to cope and still fears that people will see him as stupid. Meanwhile his drug use has escalated substantially.

ADDICTION

Whereas in the early stages of drug use people are seeking drug benefits, once they are addicted it's different: They "want to use because they want to use." They are driven by a compulsion that dominates their lives as they get more deeply involved with drugs and have bigger and bigger problems. Attaining and using drugs becomes their highest value, despite the harm their choices might inflict upon themselves, their friends, and family.

When people who are addicted stop using drugs, they go through "withdrawal," which can be an extremely unpleasant experience, both physically and psychologically. The pain and discomfort of the withdrawal process is part of what makes it so hard for them to quit if they wish to do so. A man wakes up and says "never again," vowing to quit heroin. But he can't make it through the day and finally starts using again to numb the pain. Just like countless others who say "never another drop of alcohol," but quickly start drinking. At this point, drugs are no longer used to feel good, but to prevent negative feelings – i.e., the "crash" of withdrawal. Often, all they want is to feel nothing or to numb their pain.

With addiction, there is an increased danger of poisoning or overdose, especially when drugs are used in combinations. There is also the possibility of numerous long-term health consequences, many of which are life threatening. People who use needles run the risk of serious infections (HIV, hepatitis, and others).

Extreme danger: Anyone who has gone to a 30-day rehab program for opioid addiction or has had a long period of abstinence should know that it could be medically dangerous to resume using at previous levels of use. Many overdoses occur because people resume at previous levels and do not know that their bodies' tolerance has been reduced due to abstaining.

If you have reached the level of addiction, you may be interested in knowing that the root meaning of the word "addiction" is "slave to." Addicted individuals feel as though they are slaves to drugs. They feel as if they have lost control and may see themselves as powerless over their desire. Failed attempts to gain control further reinforce the sense of powerlessness.

Sadly, social stigma compounds the pain of people who are addicted to drugs. Heaped on top of the harm from the compulsion is the judgmental way our culture condemns those who are addicted, when what they really need is understanding and compassion about their situation, and support in liberating themselves from the chains of addiction.[7]

DRUG LIFESTYLE

When drug use escalates to a very high level, a troubling pattern sometimes emerges. It's called a drug lifestyle. People may begin to associate drugs with everything in life. If they feel pain, they want drugs. If they are bored, they want drugs. If they have conflict, they want drugs. They may begin to operate on the belief that "If it feels good, do it," without consideration of other factors and other people. A type of selfishness sometimes emerges as they begin to believe "It's OK to do whatever it takes to get what you want." They mess up at home and at work or in school. They may run away, quit jobs, or drop out. They may commit crimes under the influence of drugs or to pay for them. They start behaving irresponsibly and breaking promises to themselves and others.

Sometimes people feel so guilty about their drug use or ashamed, or live in such fear of negative consequences about being "caught," that they become sneaky and secretive about what they're doing. They repeatedly lie to their spouse/romantic partners and family. They eventually lose the trust of people they love.

None of this is because they are "bad people." No one chooses to be additcted. It is a learned behavior in response to the conditions of life. If you are addicted, it is important to remember this. It is important to recognize the harmfulness of your drug use, but also engage Nurturing Self-talk in order to regain your self-respect and integrity, and connect with people who will understand and support you.

LEGAL PROBLEMS

There's a special category of harm that actually has nothing to

---

[7] *Psychologist Scott Kellogg wisely noted that if addiction to drugs means enslavement to them, then the process of overcoming addiction is liberation.*

do with the drugs themselves, and everything to do with the laws regarding drugs. That is, people may be charged and even convicted of violating drug possession laws. Arrests for possession are a problem because of legal consequences, not because of something inherent in the use of drugs.

Drug laws are arbitrary and vary in different jurisdictions and cultures. People often disagree about whether or not certain drugs should be decriminalized or legalized. We know, too, that there are enormous injustices in the enforcement of the laws; with biases, prejudices, and disparities in the arrests, convictions, and sentencing of people of color. It shouldn't be this way.

Nevertheless, drug laws exist and charges and convictions occur when people are involved with drugs. Problems with the law are another possible harmful consequence from drug use.

Some people have no problems with drugs, but problems with the courts that happen to involve drugs.

Some people have problems with drugs, but not with the courts.

Some people have problems in both realms.

Similarly, people can have problems with other types of authority: schools, places of employment, coaches, etc. that may involve drugs.

FEEDBACK FROM OTHERS

If you don't want someone else watching over you, telling you what to do, and directing your life, then you have to take charge yourself. You have to watch yourself and make your own decisions, resisting the tendency to say everything is OK (including your level of drug use) without really checking things out. As hard as you try to be self-aware and honest, people can't always see things about themselves that other people might notice. So, it's important to get the perspective of others and their feedback.

Ideally, you can find a counselor you can trust and/or someone or some people who know you well, who you trust, who won't spare you from the truth and won't put you down. You might want to talk with a friend, a trusted co-worker, a family member, a sibling, or a clergy person. Tell them the details of your drug use. Ask them if they think you have a drug problem or not, and how they reached their conclusions. If there's *not* someone to ask who knows you well, look for other people you trust or a support group in your community and tell them about your life and drug use. Let them ask questions. Give them all the facts and then ask them whether they think you have a problem or not – and on what basis they reached their conclusions. If it's hard to open up with others, then work on it. Be bold and break out of your comfort zone. Don't allow yourself to be isolated and alone. We all need and deserve support.

CHALLENGE THREE: SUMMARY AND ACTION STEPS

Challenge Three is about honestly appraising the type of harm that has occurred from your drug use, as well as the extent and seriousness of it. It's also about identifying harm that could occur: bad things that have not happened, but could happen because of the risks you take. See page 48 (It Could Happen).

It is understandable that you might have been defensive in the past when: (1) people bombarded you with the harm from drugs and tried to make you stop using them; and (2) your own Oppressive Self-talk was harshly critical of you and your drug use. Now, however, is the time to actively look for harm.

To make an honest appraisal of harm, you have to rise above the natural tendency to defend yourself both from judgmental people and your own Oppressive Self-talk. You can't *minimize*, such as "no big deal;" or *rationalize*, such as "it's because I've been having tough times;" or *make meaningless comparisons*, such as "not as bad as some other people I know;" or *accept untested assertions*, such as "I could stop whenever I want." Rather than fending off criticism, the challenge is to actively look for harm and identify all of it, in each and every aspect of your life.

NOTE: To succeed, you must have a nurturing attitude that accepts mistakes and problems as part of life. We all make them and can learn from them. If we want to improve our lives, we need to know the truth. We must not use the truth as an excuse to put ourselves down.

Action steps with Challenge Three start with writing a list about all the ways, even little ways, that alcohol and other drugs have caused harm in your life. *It's important to write everything down and be able to see it in black and white, right in front of you.*

In preparing to write your list, try to think about the bad things that have happened because of drugs or under the influence. Consider for example: Mistakes you made; times you embarrassed yourself; things you regretted you've done; irresponsible, unethical, or illegal behavior; ways you hurt other people; risks you took; damage you caused to property; times you overdosed or ended in the ER; health propblems; ways you compromised your values; money you wasted; trust with others that you lost.

Now prepare your list of the harm as it applies to the various aspects of your life listed below.

(Using a separate heading for each category, write the harm that has occurred.)

- In your love life
- In your social life with friends
- At work and in your career
- With your family
- To your health
- To your financial status
- To your reputation
- To your legal status (trouble with the law) or with some other authority
- To your self-esteem

High risk

To consider harm that "could occur," compose a list of all "high-risk behaviors" you engaged in while under the influence. You may have been lucky and escaped harm so far, but harm could occur. Here are some possibilities to consider: sex under the influence; sexually exploited or abused under the influence; physical fights under the influence; drove motor vehicles; operated machinery; gambling; spending sprees; committed a crime under the influence; had blackouts; binged and got dangerously intoxicated; overdosed; used dirty needles; been in dangerous places; been with dangerous people.

What you did not do

Make a list of problems that have gone unsolved that you might have solved (or tried to solve) if you hadn't used drugs to escape from the reality of your life. To figure this out, think about the types of situations in which you liked drugs (Challenge Two). For example, you might find that you used drugs whenever fights occurred in your romantic relationship. If you hadn't used drugs, maybe you would have worked more on your relationship problems, made progress and perhaps even solved them.

Make a list of life skills you might have learned or refined if you had not used drugs to escape from the reality of your life. Consider skills such as these: stress management, anger management, time management, relaxation skills, social skills, communication skills, or the skill of planning a good recreational life. See page 50 (The Problems With Escaping Reality).

Emerging problems

List the ways in which you are headed to trouble.

For example: Falling behind in work, but hasn't been noticed yet; lying to romantic partner who is unaware of the lying; using drugs that you said you never would use; using drugs at times or in situations that you said you would never use them. (Challenge Five is about looking to the future and will help you more clearly identify the potential for harm that lies ahead.)

Loss of control

Rate the level of control you have over your use of drugs, from one (no control at any time) to 10 (total control at all times). Write down your number. If it's less than 10, write a short paragraph about the ways in which you lack control.

Feedback from others

To make sure you don't miss anything, identify at least one person (ideally more) who knows you well and you trust to be honest and non-judgmental. This could be a counselor if you want. Honestly talk about your drug use. Disclose everything and ask this person for an opinion about the extent and seriousness of the harm that has occurred.

Your level of concern

Even if you believe that the harm from drugs may outweigh the benefits, remember that this challenge is not about decision-making. At this point, you are simply trying to uncover all the harm. What you decide to do about it, if anything, is a different matter. After thinking about harm from drugs and getting feedback from other people, consider the type of harm that has occurred, and the extent and seriousness of it. Now it is a question of your own opinion about how much harm is acceptable. The Challenging Voice will say, "No excuses. Think carefully about all the harm." Don't avoid the truth: You always have the option of seeking the help of a healthcare professional.

SAVE YOUR LISTS AND PARAGRAPH. YOU'LL WANT TO REFER TO THEM LATER.

CHALLENGE FOUR

Challenging yourself to
look at your responsibility
and the responsibility
of others for your problems

SELF BLAME

Blame and shame are among the biggest obstacles to overcoming drug problems. People blame themselves, and themselves alone, for everything. They define their drug problems in terms of personal shortcomings, and tend to ignore circumstances. They do it in the worst possible way – beating themselves up, putting themselves down, and explaining it all in terms of personal flaws.

You can observe it in their Oppressive Self-talk:

"You're stupid. Weak-willed. A failure. A loser. A druggie."

Furthermore, they say:

"It's your fault. You shouldn't have let this happen. It's all on you."

Friends, family members, acquaintances, and co-workers all too often join the choir in assigning blame.

Really, though, this sort of "all my fault" thinking isn't fair because drug problems result from multiple causes – many of which stem from the conditions of life over which individuals have little or no control. This isn't to deny the importance of personal responsibility. Of course we all share responsibility for the direction of our own lives. However, let's distribute responsibility fairly and stop taking things out of context.

Also, "all my fault" thinking isn't fair because name calling and finger pointing is a terrible thing to do, and a dead end. Yes, people who want to overcome drug problems must ultimately take personal responsibility for what they put in their bodies and for changing their own behavior. However, putting yourself down and beating yourself up prevents this from happening. It creates shame and makes people defensive.

BEATING YOURSELF UP

When things aren't going well in life, people tend to look within themselves to find flaws. They doubt their own intelligence, character, judgment, or sanity. They ask "what's-wrong-with-me" questions that reinforce strong feelings of shame and blame. When it comes to problems with alcohol and other drugs, they ask themselves:

- "How could you be so stupid (or wrong, or crazy, or bad, or selfish, or self-destructive, or harmful)?"
- "Why did you make such a stupid (or crazy, or bad, or selfish, or self-destructive, or harmful) mistake?"
- "Why did you do something so stupid (or wrong, or crazy, or bad, or selfish, or self-destructive, or harmful)?"

Oppressive thinking of this sort is treacherous: When you do it, supposedly you are addressing a sincere question: How did this happen? It sounds like rational thinking. But, really it's Oppressive Self-talk; just a sneaky way to put yourself down. Reading between the lines, the real question is: "What's wrong with you?" Looking inwardly, you're left with explanations that refer to flaws: I did it because I'm stupid, or wrong, or bad, or selfish, or self-destructive, or harmful. Oppressive Self-talk fills people with shame and makes them want to hide their problems from themselves and everyone else. They're stuck in a box with only simplistic solutions, which could be summarized as "Stop being a defective person."

When it comes to overcoming drug problems, the simplistic solutions are to be less stupid, or wrong, or selfish, or self-destructive, or harmful. That's about as helpful as "Say NO to drugs."

STOP BEATING YOURSELF UP

Why would you admit to drug problems if it only left you feeling bad about yourself and stuck in a rut with no way out? Blaming yourself for everything does just that. It leaves you paralyzed, with only simplistic solutions to complex problems. That's why it's so important to get the big picture: to understand the conditions that surround your drug use. People use drugs for a reason. If you want to understand and overcome a drug problem, stop beating yourself up and start looking for your reasons. Do it with compassion. It's hard enough to deal with the consequences of problematic drug use without the additional burden of putting yourself down and blaming yourself for everything. It's important to have Nurturing Self-talk. If you eventually make or have already made a decision to quit or set new limits, you'll need Nurturing Self-talk to sustain your efforts. Otherwise, Oppressive Self-talk will blame you for everything and beat you up every time you have a setback. You'll be discouraged and more likely to give up. In contrast, Nurturing Self-talk allows you to accept that problems and setbacks are inevitable. It builds you up to learn from them.

VALIDATION

When you stop beating yourself up about your drug problems and look closely at the conditions of your life, you'll begin to understand why you use drugs and how you reached your current level of use. There's always an explanation that makes sense.

The process of putting drug problems into the context of your life experiences is called *validation.* Instead of concluding that your problems are due to personal flaws, you look at the big picture – current conditions and the impact of past experiences – and you'll be able to make sense of your reality. You'll understand the evolution of your drug use, and be able to explain how things came to be the way that they are.

Instead of asking: "what's wrong with me," the question changes to "how did this come to be?"

When you examine your life closely, you'll reach the point where you'll be able to say: "Of course I use drugs. This explains it."

These are the: "Oh, I get it" moments. Once you "get it," it's much easier to accept your drug problems without beating yourself up.

You can say: "I see what's going on. I see how this came to be. Now I better step up to the plate and do something about it. I can't allow this to continue."

Be careful not to confuse validation with justification. You're not justifying your behavior with validation. Rather, you are understanding and explaining how it evolved.

THE "OH, I GET IT" MOMENT

A man about to be released from probation after two drug-free months suddenly smokes weed a few days before he would be free and clear. It seems to make no sense. He asks himself:

"Why would I do such a stupid thing? What's wrong with me?"

Then, with the help of a counselor, he stopped to think about it and came to this understanding:

"For days on end I had been anxious most of the night, tossing and turning for many hours before finally falling asleep. I was beyond total exhaustion. I was averaging maybe two or three hours of sleep each night and felt like I couldn't take it anymore. I was at my wit's end. Worse still, I knew that I had a difficult assignment at work the next day. I saw no relief. So I smoked before bed to get a decent night's sleep before facing what I knew would be a tough day at work."

This was his 'Oh, I get it moment.'

"I can see why I did what I did."

Did he regret it? Yes. Might there have been a better choice? Yes. Were there negative consequences? Yes. Was he aware of an alternative at the moment? No.

In his mind, he had a choice: Either be awake and sleepless for yet another night, feel miserable, worry about work; toss and turn, OR he could smoke weed and sleep and maybe even have a successful day at his job.

The circumstances of this man's life simply overwhelmed his ability to cope with them.

Did his explanation of the circumstances justify what he did? No. It was not meant to justify it – simply to understand it.

When you look at your life in context, you can see why you have been doing what you've been doing. You can also think about what you could do to improve the situation.

Once this sleep-deprived man realized what had happened, he could face reality.

"It's definitely a problem that I smoked weed. I didn't want to smoke it, but now I see why I did. Now I see that I need to work on my sleeping problem. I also need to work on my problem with anxiety because that's what keeps me awake at night. I'll focus on these issues in the weeks ahead. Either I do that, or I'm stuck relying on drugs. Maybe the sleep problem won't be fixed quickly, so in the meantime, I need to think about how I'll handle sleepless nights. I'm going to make a plan."

He decided to do relaxing activities before bedtime, to get counseling for his anxiety, and that he might use short-term medication, like Tylenol PM®. He was determined to avoid another relapse.

BOMBARDED WITH DRUG MESSAGES

Taking a step back from our own little world, we can see that we live in a consumer-oriented society, with countless messages – media and personal – telling us to buy and consume. "If you feel bad, buy this. Want to stop feeling bad? Buy that. If you don't like the way you look, buy this. If you don't want to be outdone by your neighbor, buy that. Want to feel good? Eat this." Also, whenever you buy, be sure it's the latest model and the newest gadget. In our society, we face relentless pressure to consume – always with an implied promise to feel better.

This pressure to consume extends to drugs. By the time you read this book, you will have received countless messages to use drugs: Doctors always have a pill to offer. "Feel bad? Take one of these." The pharmaceutical industry spends millions and millions of dollars promoting their products with massive advertising campaigns. They tell us to pester our doctors to get their drugs. Modern psychiatry is drug driven, with psychiatrists prescribing pills to everyone from the youngest children right through to the most elderly. Pediatricians keep a patient list as well as a list of pharmaceutical representatives (reps)…all waiting for time with the doctor. In the past, big tobacco pushed cigarettes. Now they promote vaping. Meanwhile, the alcohol industry has never relented, promising good times, status, and fun.

We have been bombarded with messages to use drugs to change the way we feel. Don't think for a second that this consumer-oriented society doesn't affect your desire to use alcohol and other drugs. It's not a surprise that so many people end up with drug problems. If you've been having them, as you try to truly understand your own situation, be aware that you've been inundated with massive drug propaganda.

THE CONDITIONS OF YOUR LIFE: PAIN

Consider the impact of the world around you on your drug use. We know, for example, that people use drugs to cope with stress. So, it's not surprising that a large percentage of people with drug problems have been victimized by physical, sexual, or emotional abuse. Consider, too, the impact of unemployment; or boring or physically exhausting work; or living in poverty and struggling to pay the rent and buy food. Think, too, of the stress that racism imposes on people of color. Think of the stress related to the treatment of non-traditional sexual orientations or gender identities. Think of the stress that all these harsh conditions produce.

However, you don't have to be down on your luck or beaten to death by dramatic, oppressive circumstances to explain why you turn to drugs at problematic levels. Sometimes it's just the grind of everyday work that takes its toll. Sometimes it's loneliness. Sometimes it's a joyless life, with no visible path to feeling better. Sometimes it's the unhappiness of feeling trapped in conflict-ridden relationships or families, without a clue about how to fix things. Sometimes it's a sense of meaninglessness or disappointment in life. Sometimes it's the psychological pain of an enduring depressed mood or intense anxiety, without clear immediate causes or a visible remedy. Sometimes it's just boredom or a sense that life has no purpose.

Everyone's story is different. We each have our own unique constellation of stressors. Some stressors are due to our situation and others are internal, emotional and less obvious, such as personal pain and anguish. We each have different vulnerabilities. What affects one person might not affect another in the same way. We also differ in available resources to cope with this stress, including which life skills and coping mechanisms we have had the opportunity to learn.

Although each person's story is unique, they all have one thing in common: Drug problems can occur when the difficulties of our circumstances exceed our ability to cope with them. It will be very important to think about this when trying to make changes in your drug use behavior. On one hand, this explains how the drug problems arose and takes away some of the crippling sting of guilt and excessive self-blame. On the other hand, you will find you have tough situations to face. Massive willpower can help you resist drugs, but you can't overlook the tough situations. You have to consider making substantial changes in other aspects of your life. To put it bluntly, if you're miserable in your life and use drugs to mask it, when you stop using drugs you'll still feel miserable. So prepare yourself for confronting more issues. Look at what is making you miserable and figure out what you can do about it. If you feel stuck, go out and get help from others, including professional counselors.

THE CONDITIONS OF YOUR LIFE: PLEASURE

Drug use isn't always about escaping pain. Sometimes it's about seeking pleasure. Drugs give a spark when life seems dull, mundane, or boring. They can be something to look forward to…at the end of the day or a work week. Drugs can provide fun, a thrill, or an altered state of consciousness. They are especially appealing to people who have little else in life that seems to offer a positive alternative for pleasure. That's why circumstances are important to consider. Some people never had an opportunity to learn how to build a good recreational and/or social life. Many people currently live in environments in which few other affordable sources of pleasure are available. Under these circumstances, drugs fill the void.[8]

In thinking about your own drug use, consider your options for pleasure and your own capacity to make fun things happen without drugs. If your drug use has been problematic, this could be a factor.

PRIVILEGISM: THE DOWNSIDE OF HAVING EVERYTHING

When you talk about the connection between environment and drug use, most of us think first about oppression and oppressive circumstances. However, other circumstances at the exact opposite end of the economic spectrum – among individuals who grew up wealthy and privileged – can also contribute to drug problems. Coming from affluent and powerful families, these individuals face

---

[8]*In his insightful book "High Price", psychologist Carl Hart reveals how lack of pleasure and other types of positive reinforcers are such a strong influence on problematic drug use.*

a unique and sometimes difficult type of challenge: Living with the consequences of having everything. They expect to feel good all the time, and to have every need satisfied without any effort. In this regard, drugs work very well for them.

Growing up rich and indulged is most definitely not oppression, but for some people it could be called "privilegism." Though privileged in most regards, some of these individuals were denied an opportunity to understand the connection between effort and success. Everything was given to them. Some of them were denied an opportunity to develop character: They felt selfishly entitled to anything they wanted, without regard to others. Some were coddled and over-protected, consistently rescued from hard work and negative consequences. When they got in trouble, their families bailed them out. They wrecked a car and their parents bought them a new one. They never faced adversity and so could not develop resilience. As adults, many suffered the consequences of these early experiences. Lacking resourcefulness, they had troubled lives.

Another form of privilegism occurs when successful and affluent parents put enormous pressure on their children by demanding unreasonable levels of achievement. Under this pressure, their children fear they could never meet their parents' expectations. This creates overwhelming anxiety and can lead to drug problems that continue into young adulthood and beyond.

In stark contrast to those young people who managed poorly, there are individuals from affluent families who took advantage of the numerous opportunities that presented themselves. They became successful by conventional standards (social and economic class status) and continued to prosper. Many of them felt content. However, even among the "successful," there were some who felt a sense of emptiness. They attained material success, but not happiness or satisfaction in life. This could be confusing, too, because they felt like they "had everything" and should be happy. However, deep inside their lives felt empty. Something was missing. Some of them turned to drugs. (This same problem also occurs among less privileged individuals, with fewer opportunities, who manage to climb the social ladder on their own and achieve comparable success. They were driven by the belief that economic prosperity and high status would give them what they wanted in life, but it didn't.)

EXCUSES

There are always reasons for drug problems and it's important to understand your own. When you begin to explain the ways in which the conditions of your life have influenced your drug use behavior, be prepared for an onslaught of protest from both your own Oppressive Self-talk and other people around you.

"It's your fault," the critics will say. "Don't make excuses!"

What the critics fail to understand is that you're not making excuses. Rather you're seeking to understand your situation – how things came to be. This sort of understanding dramatically reduces shame. Also, once you know why you have done what you've been doing, you are better prepared to decide on your next steps.

"Stop trying to justify things," the critics protest.

You're not trying to justify anything. You're not saying your drug use is OK (or, for that matter, not OK). All you're saying is that you can see how it came to be the way it is. You are seeking understanding. Validation is not the same as justification.

"Take responsibility for what you are doing."

You're not denying responsibility. Of course we all contribute to our own circumstances in life. We're not passive bystanders. However, some circumstances are beyond our control. We can determine our own responsibility only when we get the whole picture. Then we know what happened. Then we can break it down.

"Well, you have a part in this, too."

Of course you do. We all play a part in creating our own circumstances. But that doesn't mean that we can understand our problems, including drug problems, without considering everything else that is going on.

QUIT COMPLAINING

"Hey," you may hear someone say, "Plenty of people come from the same harsh conditions as you, and they're doing just fine. Quit complaining." Those who make statements such as this just don't get it. You're not saying that your life is pre-determined by circumstances. It's not a gripe session. You're simply saying that you are affected by circumstances. You're not comparing yourself to other people. Anyway, no two sets of circumstances are exactly the same. For example, you can live in poverty and have completely different stories. You could have a parent who is very loving and determined to help you in school. By the same token, you could have a parent who is depressed, self-absorbed (or pre-occupied trying to make ends meet), can't show affection, and uninvolved in your schooling. You could be a first-born, a middle-child, or the "baby" of a family. You could be male or female. It's ridiculous to say that two people have the "same circumstances." It's just more finger pointing and blaming. Everyone has a different story.

It's definitely not a level playing field. Just because one person or some people can transcend difficult circumstances, doesn't mean everyone can. Most people don't. When you are a person of color or growing up in poverty, you certainly start with more stress than others. Sexism and homophobia take their toll. On a personal level, family strife and tension profoundly affect children. These are facts.

If your circumstances are stressful, or harm your self-esteem, or lower your expectations, then they are part of your story and influence your history. This fact can't be overlooked. If you want self-understanding, you need the whole picture. You've got to consider both the impact of your current situation and the lingering influences from the past. This allows you to see the whole picture and puts you in a position to understand your own history, and to maximize control over the direction of your life right now.

BLAME THE WORLD FOR EVERYTHING

More often than not, people unfairly blame themselves for everything that goes wrong in their lives. Sometimes, though, they go in the opposite direction and blame the world for everything. To be fair, some of these people have good cause to be angry about the hands they were dealt. However, simply sitting around and blaming the world won't make their personal lives any better. It's important to avoid this trap and use your personal power to confront reality.

If you're waiting for the world to change, I hope you have a comfortable armchair because it's going to be a long wait. Although you're influenced and can be limited by circumstances, you do not have to be fully controlled by them. Recognizing the impact of circumstances helps you put everything in context, so you don't beat yourself up. Once you understand the whole picture of how your current situation evolved, you can strap on your boots and do the best you can to make things better. Moving forward, you choose what to do.

When you recognize you have a drug problem and want a better life, it's ultimately up to you to take action. In part this means making decisions to either stop using drugs or to keep within the limits you set. Although support helps, only you can make this change.

SHARED RESPONSIBILITY

"You create your own reality." Have you heard this one? This is really just a sneaky way of being blamed (or blaming yourself) for everything. Try saying that, for example, to someone who was raised in poverty by a single parent who was both physically and emotionally abusive. Did this person create his or her own reality? Of course not. No one does.

There are numerous circumstances that impact our lives. This doesn't mean we're powerless, passive bystanders as our lives roll by. We do our best within our range of possibilities. We have choices. We can make matters worse or improve our situation. Sometimes we cope well. Sometimes we make our own predicaments worse. It would be fair to say that we *help* create our own reality. We play a part in it and bear some responsibility. By the same token, we have power to make changes.

When we see ways in which we disappoint ourselves, or that we are hurting ourselves or others, we need to take responsibility for what we are doing. It's important to take action to make things better.

HARM TO OTHERS

Problematic drug use often incudes causing harm to other people.

The harm could be widespread and serious. It might include, for example: stealing, hurting, and lying to people you love; damaging relationships in your family; financial harm to your family; failure to take care of parental, family, or workplace responsibilities; harm to your employer; dangerous or criminal behavior while under the influence; committing crimes to pay for drugs; or harm caused by legal problems that affect friends and family.

If you have been harming others it will be important to recognize this reality and take responsibility, which would include stopping the harmful behavior, apologizing when appropriate, and possibly repairing the harm. You can't undo what was done, but you can open the possibility of moving forward in a positive way by making a heartfelt apology, expressing sincere regret, and ideally, by saying what you learned that would help you do better in the future.

Beating yourself up won't help. Oppressive Self-talk will put you down for hurting others – keep you mired in guilt. Watch for that and be ready to fight back. It will be important to use Nurturing Self-talk, which reassures you that mistakes are part of life and that you can learn from them and do better in the future. All you can do is do your best.

DRUG-NEEDINESS QUOTIENT

Many drug treatment programs include a component in which people "tell their story,' which means give the history of their drug use, emphasizing the harm, as it progressed from when it first started to the present time. However, they leave out an enormously important part: To really tell your drug story, you need to go back to *before* the problem started and consider the circumstances. In particular, consider (1) what was going on in your life and (2) the limits of your ability to manage or cope with those circumstances. This will uncover your vulnerabilities.

You can think of it this way: You could say that you have a Drug-Neediness Quotient (DNQ). We all have difficulties in life (pain, worries, discomfort, troubles, disappointments, etc.). Your DNQ is determined by two things:

- The level of stress and difficulties in your life
- Your ability to solve problems and cope with difficulties.

If you *don't* have extraordinary difficulties and you *do* have well-developed problem solving and coping skills, you would have a very low DNQ. On the other hand, if you *do* have extraordinary difficulties and *don't* have well-developed problem solving and coping skills, you would have an extremely high DNQ. Most of us fall somewhere between these two extremes.

You might find that considering your own DNQ is a helpful way to think about a drug problem. It shows that the problem can be addressed both by overcoming some of the difficulties in your life and by developing better problem solving and coping skills. When you lower your DNQ in this manner, it becomes increasingly possible to change your drug use behavior. It's a way to start.

CHALLENGE FOUR: SUMMARY AND ACTION STEPS

Challenge Four is about shared responsibility. People tend to beat themselves up and blame themselves for everything that has gone wrong in their lives. This challenge helps you look at the conditions of your life and make sense of your experiences in a fair and supportive way.

"Oh, I Get It" moments (page 62) occur when you can explain your drug use in the context of everything else that is happening in your life, including your story of how it evolved to the current (or most problematic) level. See also page 62 (Validation).

The most basic action step with Challenge Four is to take account of the conditions of your life that have contributed to your drug use. There is a tendency for people to overlook these conditions. Don't do that. Instead prepare a list of the circumstances and conditions – past and present – that contribute to your drug use. Take account of ways you were treated that were unfair or oppressive or unfortunate, and of opportunities that you were denied. Also include the everyday problems and stress that you have faced and are currently facing.

Using your list of conditions, write a one paragraph "story before your story." See page 71 (Drug-Neediness Quotient) telling how the conditions of your life, including stress of all sorts, have led to your current drug use. This is not to blame the world for everything, just to explain how things came to be. If your drug use reached problematic levels, there is a story that explains it.

Write a paragraph about the ways in which your drug use has harmed other people. See page 70 (Harm To Others).

SAVE YOUR LIST AND PARAGRAPHS. YOU'LL WANT TO REFER TO THEM LATER.

CHALLENGE FIVE

Challenging yourself to look at where
you are headed, where you would like to go,
and what you would like to accomplish

FAIRY TALES

We all start life with fairy tales and dreams about the future.

Then reality strikes…and it's a different reality for everyone. We look around and see what our own world looks like. It might be rich and filled with opportunity. It might be foreclosed with little hope and inspiration. We might be accepted or not accepted by people around us; encouraged or discouraged; provided with opportunity or denied opportunity; supported or left all alone.

All of this affects how we view the future, including the extent to which we feel we have power over our own destiny.

Fortunate people feel that they have lots of power and the capacity to strive toward their dreams. Less fortunate ones give up on their dreams, see no future and feel stuck. Some of them want to control their future, but don't see how they could. They feel hopeless. They need encouragement. Other people try to control their future, but can't. Defeated, they feel powerless and give up. At this point, they need to try new strategies and get additional support.

If you want the best possible life for yourself, *you need to have a sense of future*. You need to gain, maintain, or regain your belief in your own personal power. You can't give up. You need hope and optimism. It's a tall task, especially for those who have been discouraged, denied opportunity, or insufficiently supported. Nevertheless, it can be done. It's not a level playing field, but with a full-blown effort and the support of others, you can transcend your circumstances and make a better life.

A SENSE OF FUTURE

You have a choice. You could coast through life in the here-and-now, accepting whatever presents itself; living in the moment. You wouldn't have to think much about the future, or consciously take action to influence it. Sure you'd make decisions, but not with much forethought. Circumstances would pretty much determine your destiny. If you were lucky, life would be OK. If not, things would slide downhill.

The alternative is to take action to direct your life. You could strive for mastery and control. You could try to make things go the way you want them to go. To succeed, you would need clarity about what you want out of life and an optimistic sense that you could make it happen.

Unfortunately, many people have had numerous setbacks and failure experiences. They resign themselves to fate. Nothing will improve for them until they regain a sense of future and build or rebuild their self-confidence about shaping it. Challenge Five provides you with an opportunity to do just that!

THE RIGHT-NOW BRAIN

One of the biggest obstacles to thinking ahead to the future is the "right-now brain" we have inherited from our primitive ancestors. This brain of ours has not evolved as quickly as the circumstances of human lives have changed.

In primitive times, when people roamed nomadically in search of scarce food, they seized every opportunity to eat when they saw fruit on a tree, or berries on a bush, or a source of meat. Their survival depended upon it. Our brains at the present time are still influenced by this "here and now" approach to life. You could say: "If it's hanging from a tree, pick it and eat it." We seek immediate gratification.

Psychological experiments show that people will choose small rewards (money or whatever) in the immediate moment over waiting, even short periods of time, for substantially bigger rewards.

Our right-now brain, designed to grab available food, carries the same tendency over to all sorts of consumer items, pleasures, and positive experiences. We tend to do whatever is easiest and feels good in the moment. When opportunities present themselves, we want to indulge without concern about consequences or how it might affect our future.

The right-now brain is all about immediate satisfaction. It doesn't address the very important question: *"And then what happens?"* Nothing wrong with seeking pleasure, but in making *informed choices* about what we do, potential consequences must also be considered.

THE RIGHT-NOW BRAIN ON DRUGS

Our right-now brain wants immediate gratification. Drugs offer just that – instant pleasure (or relief from pain) in the here and now – a great attraction to the not-fully-evolved brain. Drugs work wonders if you live for the moment. You can feel happy, brave, energetic, or nothing at all. Drugs can stop you from feeling angry, scared, sad, or hurt. They can give you control over what you feel.

We all know, however, that uncontrolled "right-now pleasure" can get us in trouble. Bad things can happen when we indulge to excess. This isn't to say that all drug use is harmful – simply that we must consider the potential for harm.

If you want to resist the right-now brain that seeks pleasure all the time without regard to future consequences, don't start thinking it'll be easy. Don't underestimate the power of our primitive brain. It's a force of nature. The right-now brain wants drugs and more drugs. That's one reason why it's so hard to change drug use behavior. If you want to succeed, you'll have to rely on a different part of your brain that allows you to think about consequences and think ahead to the future.

ADDICTION: THE RIGHT-NOW BRAIN "GONE WILD"

Drugs provide the instant pleasure and immediate gratification that our right-now brain wants. When you use a drug, you get the reward. This is called positive reinforcement. Each time a behavior is rewarded, it becomes more likely that it will be repeated. Psychologists have called this process *operant conditioning*. Because drugs can be enormously powerful reinforcers, they make resisting the unevolved right-now brain extra hard. Operant conditioning can lead to addiction, in which the right-now brain "gone wild" becomes the monkey on your back!

As if that's not enough, think about the famous experiment conducted by Ivan Pavlov, the Russian psychologist. He knew that dogs salivate when they are fed. So in his experiment, he rang a bell every time he was feeding the dogs. The bell would ring, food would be served, and the dogs would salivate. The dogs learned that when the bell rings, food would be coming. Soon they were conditioned to the bell ringing. Whenever the bell rang, even *without* food, they would salivate. This is called *classical conditioning* (or Pavlovian conditioning).

Consider how classical conditioning applies to drugs. If you use drugs when you feel anxious, you begin to condition yourself. It goes like this: You feel anxious. You use a drug. The anxiety is relieved. Anxiety and drugs are paired together. Do it enough and it becomes a conditioned response: Whenever you feel anxious, you will feel like using a drug. So, if you ever decide to stop using drugs or set new limits, you will continue to have strong urges to use them whenever you feel anxious. You could say that anxiety now "rings your bell." People condition themselves in many ways: When they see certain friends, it rings their bell. When they feel bored, it rings their bell. When they go to a party; it rings their bell. When they can't sleep at night: it rings their bell. This type of conditioning makes it so very difficult to change drug use behavior. It tightens the grip of the right-now brain.

THE SMART BRAIN

While a chunk of our brain remains in its more primitive stage, other parts of it have evolved and can compensate for the risky nature of our pleasure seeking tendencies. Fortunately we have a very well developed part – the "smart brain" – that allows us to think rationally and go beyond the simple pursuit of pleasure (or relief from pain).[9] The smart brain allows us to think about our future – to really think deeply about what's important to us...what we want out of life. It also allows us to think carefully about the present time, as well. It looks at the full impact (whole picture) of the choices we make, including the immediate and future consequences. It recognizes the immediate pleasure, but deepens the conversation by asking: "And then what happens?"

With regard to drugs, it asks the important questions: Are there negative consequences? What are they? What might happen? What usually happens? How will drug use at the present time affect the near and distant future?

In fully evaluating your own drug use, the smart brain helps you consider many factors, including what you like about the drugs in

---

[9] *If you want to get scientific, the smart brain is the pre-frontal cortex.*

the here and now (Challenge Two), the immediate harm (Challenge Three), as well as the way in which drug use would affect the future that you want for yourself (Challenge Five).

Here's the catch. You have to activate the smart brain.[10] When you're flying on automatic pilot, the right-now brain rules. It's the fast brain; the impulsive part that immediately says: "Grab that. Eat this. Buy that. Smoke this. Drink this. Just do it." Before you know it, you're doing exactly what it says, unless…you say STOP! SLOW DOWN…AND THINK! That's your power of self-control. It's the moment when you slow things down and activate your smart brain. When you can consistently do this, you gain control over your life.

"YES (IT FEELS GOOD), BUT…"

The smart brain slows the right-now brain's relentless pursuit of *immediate* pleasure. It examines the full impact of drug use, including harm and potential harm.

A handy way of notating harm from drugs is with a format that starts with the sentence stem: "Yes, but..." followed by a list of (1) the bad things that will happen because of problematic drug use as well as (2) the good things that *won't* happen.

"Yes, but…" statements point out both the immediate, short-term negative consequences of problematic drug use and the long-term negative impact. They describe what is likely to happen in the next moment, next day, next week, six months from now, a year from now, ten years from now, and as far down the line as you would like to project.

Here's the prototype: "Yes, if I use drugs I will immediately feel good, *but* this will (or would, or could) cause harm."

Here are some examples:

- Yes, I could drink freely and feel good (relieve my stress and feel more comfortable in a social gathering), *but* I tend to embarrass myself and get in trouble when I drink.

---

[10] *"Thinking Fast and Slow," by Daniel Kahneman, introduced the idea of two types of thinking*

- Yes, I could keep partying and having fun, *but* my use is escalating and I might harm my body and end up with a drug problem.
- Yes, I could keep doctor shopping and getting more pills or even switch to heroin, *but* I am losing control of my life, spending outrageous sums of money, hurting my body, and could even kill myself with these painkillers.
- Yes, I can make this awful emotional pain go away with drugs, *but* if I do that I'll remain addicted and drugs will continue to rule my life.

To counter your own right-now brain, try to compose as many "Yes, but..." statements as you can.

WALKING AWAY FROM PLEASURE

Why would anyone in their right mind walk away from the immediate pleasure that drugs provide?

Only the smart brain can answer that; and one of the best answers is: You walk away if there is something that is more important to you. In other words, your immediate pleasure might be at the expense of some consequence that concerns you. To recognize this, you need to engage your smart brain: "OK, you have fun and feel good ... and then what happens?"

For example: You use drugs at work to make things tolerable and even have a laugh or two; but you don't get your work done, act a bit weird, and get in trouble with your boss. Maybe it's not worth it.

It's all about what comes next – in the future – after the pleasure. To protect against the right-now brain "gone-wild," turn your attention away from the immediate pleasure and direct it toward the future. Problematic drug use definitely has consequences. When the immediate pleasure from drug use comes at the expense of harmful consequences and/or interferes with your progress toward something that's important to you, it may not be worth it.

Why walk away from drugs? Maybe you value good health, but your drug use could mess it up. Maybe you want to achieve success in school or work, but your drug use could interfere. Maybe you want to be a good parent, but drugs could prevent you from performing your functions adequately. Maybe you want to stay out of legal trouble, but drugs could get you into the court system. These could all be reasons to walk away from drugs.

Unfortunately the unevolved right-now brain sometimes overwhelms the human ability to look ahead. When people lose sight of the future, they lose control of their destiny, and their lives end up being overly determined by circumstances and people other than themselves.

You need to constantly remind yourself to ask the crucial question: "And then what happens?"

A SENSE OF PERSONAL POWER

There's no point in thinking about the future if you don't feel that you have any control over it!

Even with clarity about what you want to achieve, you still have to believe that you could succeed; that your goals are attainable. Otherwise, it's easy to ignore the possibility of future consequences and live only for the moment. People won't set up goals, or stick with them, if they don't believe that they could succeed. That's why you need a nurturing "you can do it" voice that encourages you to achieve your goals. But this can't be an idle affirmation. You also need to have the commitment and skills (or the confidence and ability to learn the skills) required for success.

People who have been beaten down with repeated setbacks and failure find it hard to feel confident. They tend to lose sight of their goals and forget what's important to them.

If you've lost confidence in yourself, then you will have to build it up again or run the risk of being overwhelmed by the right-now brain. One way to do that is by using the mastery approach to life – identify your issues, one by one, (things that are not going well or as well as you would like them to be going) – and take action on them to make things better. As you make little improvements, one after another, you begin to gain mastery and build self-confidence. If you want help, counseling can be a powerful aid to assist you in regaining control of your life.

DRUGS AND REGAINING SELF-CONFIDENCE

Maybe you've been partying too much. Maybe too many painkillers. Maybe constantly numbing yourself from the stress of daily life, or drinking away your sorrows. Drug problems can escalate to the point where you feel discouraged and ready to give up. Don't do that. Fight back.

Feeling powerless or hopeless is not the same as being powerless or hopeless. You have to believe in yourself. You have to see a better life. Focusing on what you want in life – beyond immediate pleasure and relief from pain – allows you to resist the right-now brain. Sometimes visualizing a better future or aspiring to make things better requires courage: a leap of power to think that you could succeed. Try to keep in mind what will happen if you *don't* go for it, don't take the leap, and don't make changes. The right-now brain can wreak havoc. Remember, people do harness their personal power. They can recover from problems and regain self-confidence. It's not easy, but it's doable if you accept the challenge. Plus, you can get support. You don't have to do it alone.

WHAT YOU WANT FOR YOURSELF

Do you remember saving money as a child to buy something special you really wanted? Remember how exciting that was? You set a goal and then achieved it. You could have spent your nickels and dimes buying candy, but you decided to save your money instead. We humans inherit a rational brain that can think ahead to the future. It allows us to plan and chart our course. With this capacity, it makes sense to think about what we want in life.

Close your eyes and allow yourself to dream. Try to picture life as you would like it to be. Take time to think seriously about it. What sort of person do you want to be? What type of relationships and family do you want to have? What sort of work would you like to be doing? What do you want for yourself six months from now, a year from now, ten years from now, and in the distant future?

What do you want to accomplish?

You can ask yourself: What is important to me? What are my hopes? Dreams? Desires? Goals? What do I hold important in life? What are my ambitions (things I want to accomplish)?

When you're clear about what you want in life, you can use this information to analyze your situation.

- It can help you look at where you're headed and see how that stacks up with your hopes and aspirations.
- It can help guide your evaluation of how drugs have affected your plans to date.
- It can help you see how continued drug use might affect your efforts to achieve what you want in the future.

THE SMART BRAIN WITH A SENSE OF PURPOSE

After injuring his back at work, a young man who was having some success and happiness in life got a prescription for a painkiller. This not only alleviated his pain, but also created a pleasant, happy mood. He hopped out of bed and began walking around his hometown, delighting in everything he saw. As the back problem quickly subsided, he started taking the remaining pills for fun on a daily basis for about two weeks. He loved the carefree feeling and looked forward to his indulgence every late afternoon after work, and on weekends. However, he also had Nurturing Self-talk in the form of the Challenging Voice that cautioned him: "Much as you like this, it's not really a good habit to run with. It won't work on the long run." He started thinking how his drug use could evolve into a problem (building a tolerance to the pills; needing more for the same effect; having to obtain the pills illegally after finishing the initial supply). He realized that his strong attraction to the drug could possibly interfere with everything else he wanted in life. So, he slowed the pace considerably as he enjoyed the rest of his prescription, and then stopped when the bottle was empty. Since that time, when opioids have been medically prescribed for pain, occasionally he will indulge a bit. But things never get out of control. He balances his present life and desire for pleasure with his values and plans for the future.

This young man was fortunate that he had other activities and plans that were important to him. He had a sense of meaning and direction in life. Without this, he might have continued using the prescription drugs or even switched to heroin. His drug use could have escalated as his body's tolerance increased. He might have gained immediate pleasure in his daily life in exchange for a compromised and perhaps grim future. Instead he used his smart brain to counter his right-now brain that wanted to keep indulging in a potentially dangerous way.

Not everyone has this foresight: The mindless right-now brain can wreak havoc. However your smart brain can resist it at any time by thinking these three thoughts: (1) There's a reason to resist my right-now brain because (2) drug use of this sort stands in the way of something more important to me (something I want in life) and (3) I can achieve my goals (and attain what is important to me).

Recognizing the potential for dire consequences and thinking ahead to the future is the most powerful antidote to the right-now brain that seeks immediate gratification.

THE CRITICAL QUESTION

Our unevolved brain wants the good things: There's nothing inherently wrong with seeking pleasure or relief from pain. Problems only occur when the "discussion" ends with the right-now brain in charge, without considering consequences.

When making decisions about drug use, Nurturing Self-talk in the form of a Challenging Voice looks beyond immediate pleasure. Instead of simply asking, "Will it feel good," the critical question becomes *"Will it be good for me?"*

Here's what this means in practice:

- In evaluating *a single episode of drug use*: "Will the benefits outweigh the immediate and long term consequences?"
- In evaluating *an on-going pattern of drug use*: "Do the benefits of my current pattern of use outweigh the harm and potential harm?"

Nurturing Self-talk supports you in making rational, fully informed decisions with your best interest at heart. If the benefits of drug use do not outweigh the harm, then it wants to resist the right-now brain.

OPPRESSIVE SELF-TALK

If you determine that your drug use is not in your best interest, then only Oppressive Self-talk would urge you to continue: "Just keep doing it."

Nurturing Self-talk counters by saying: "But it's not good for me. It'll mess up my life. Bad things will happen."

This rational response could release the full fury of Oppressive Self-talk, which can take multiple forms:

- "You can't stop. You can't resist. You can't change." (Powerlessness)
- "Nothing's gonna get better. Nothing will improve. Just give up." (Hopelessness).
- "Don't even think about it. Enjoy it while you can." (Mindlessness)

There's more mindlessness, too. It comes disguised in the form of resignation, as in "I don't care," which really means:

"Don't think about consequences: Ignore them. Forget what you know."

Many people mired in drug problems say they "don't care" as they watch their dreams vanish. But deep down inside they do. It's just too overwhelming or painful to think about it.

Oppressive Self-talk can sometimes take the form of *wishful thinking*; another obstacle to confronting a bad situation. It presents itself in the form of passivity: "Things will take care of themselves" (as if by magic). In other words, don't even try to do anything about your situation. Everything will magically self-correct on its own. (This is akin to quitting a job and basing a retirement plan on winning the super-lotto or waiting for Santa Claus or the tooth fairy.) Nothing wrong with hoping for the best, but wishful thinking of this sort prevents people from doing anything that could help their own cause.

Is any of this Oppressive Self-talk familiar to you? This talk allows problem behavior to continue when it's not really in your best interest. Once you understand how Oppressive Self-talk works, you can see the importance of resisting it. You can develop powerful responses by using Nurturing Self-talk that focuses on taking control of your life:

"I need to take action and I can succeed with it. If I don't take action, the problem will persist and possibly get worse."

As the saying goes: "Fake it till you make it." You may not feel that you could succeed, but act on the possibility of success regardless.

THE BATTLE

People describe the battle within themselves: The powerful, emotional right-now brain says, "Go for it," disregarding any possible harm. The mild-mannered and ever-so-reasonable smart brain asks: "And then what happens?"

Oppressive Self-talk adds fuel to the impulsive and *uncontrolled* right-now brain. In contrast, Nurturing Self-talk wants to engage the good judgment of your smart brain to protect you from harm. However, unless it gets a boost of some sort, the right-now brain will win this internal battle – hands down: It's very difficult to think rationally when the immediate rewards are instinctual and so very compelling. But, it's important to resist the right-now brain. You need to slow down the decision-making process and mount a fearsome challenge. Nurturing Self-talk must speak with power. Otherwise, attention will focus on immediate pleasure (or relief from distress) without regard to the possibility of harm. You can learn more about this in Challenge Seven, and get counseling help if you want it.

DOUBTERS AND RESCUERS

If you have had drug problems, you've probably been exposed to people who doubt you. You may doubt yourself. Difficult and discouraging life experiences eat away at your self-confidence and diminish dreams about the future. It's easy to give up.

Feelings of powerlessness lend themselves well to "rescue situations" in which the people around you want to save you from your drug problems. Some of them want to fix your life. Deep down inside, they are doubters. They see you as a weak and helpless victim in need of a rescue. Truth is: No one can save you from a drug problem. If you have one, you have to step up to the plate yourself. You have to invest the effort, maybe a massive effort, to make the desired change. People who try to fix things for you stand in your way. They collude with your feelings of powerlessness, with their implied message: "You need me to save you."

However, you *don't* have to solve problems alone. You can get support from people who respect and care about you. Rather than 'saving you,' these people believe in you and that you can make changes. They offer their help as back-up to your efforts.

Rescuing can take another form. Some rescuers actually promote drug use in their misguided efforts to save you from the pain and consequences of your actions. They provide the wherewithal for you to continue on a dangerous course with drugs. They cover your expenses, bail you out of trouble, and provide aid and resources of all sorts that allow you to maintain a harmful pattern of drug use. They simply enable the status quo. Although it is important to provide material support to people who have *decided to change and invested an effort to make change happen*, such support harms people who are mired in a negative spiral, with no intent to do anything about it.

Truly helpful, supportive people step out of the rescue role and expect you to rise to the occasion. They are warm and nurturing. They show genuine concern and say: "I'll back you up in any way that I can if you make a sincere effort to overcome your drug problem. However, I won't participate in, or contribute to, your downfall."

ANOTHER LEAP

In general, people begin to think about quitting or setting new limits on their drug use when they get a sense that the harm outweighs the benefits. They know something is wrong. They want to eliminate a problem, but still may not see an alternative. They're not likely to make changes or stick with them unless they believe that something better is possible; that it's really worth the effort.

To move forward with drug changes, you need hope, vision and optimism about a better future. You need self-confidence that you could attain it; or at least that it's a possibility. What ultimately drives people to fully commit and succeed in overcoming drug problems is having a vision of a better life – maybe with more satisfying work, a loving relationship, a close family, or whatever it is that matters to them. They see a light at the end of the tunnel. So, if you want to overcome a drug problem, you not only have to take a leap of power with regard to drugs, but also a leap with regard to building a satisfying life without drugs (or with less drugs).

It is vitally important to have a vision of a better life and determination to attain it.

CHALLENGE FIVE: SUMMARY AND ACTION STEPS

Challenge Five offers an alternative to the unevolved right-now brain that seeks immediate pleasure and relief from pain. You can walk away from these drug benefits when there is (1) something more important to you; (2) you have the confidence and power to go for it, and (3) your drug use would stand in the way of achieving what you want. Write as many "Yes, but..." statements as you can. See page 80.

An important action step with Challenge Five begins with using your imagination to picture life as you would like it to be. Often it helps to write down your thoughts about the sort of person you want to be; the type of relationships and family you want to have; and the type of work you would like to be doing. What is important to you? What do you want to accomplish? See page 83 (What You Want For Yourself).

Now write a paragraph about how your drug use has affected and could affect your chances of making your life the way you want it to be. Consider how it could be a barrier and erode some of your possibilities. Knowing the impact of drug use upon your future is part of the decision making process when comparing the costs and the benefits of your options.

In order to go for what you want in life, you have to feel that you could succeed. What does your Oppressive Self-talk say that doubts you and holds you back? See page 20 (Self-Talk) and page 22 (Oppressive Self-Talk About Drugs). Write down overwhelmingly powerful responses to that voice. See page 87 (The Battle).

If you have difficulties with these action steps, you can talk about them with trusted friends, confidants, or counselors. Don't ever give up. Go for professional help if you are distressed or feel stuck.

SAVE YOUR PARAGRAPH AND ANSWERS TO THE OPPRESSIVE VOICE. YOU'LL WANT TO REFER TO THEM LATER.

CHALLENGE SIX

Challenging yourself to make
thoughtful decisions about your life,
including your use of alcohol and other drugs

DECISIONS TO CHANGE

In gaining mastery over your own life, you constantly face situations in which you must decide what to do. Basically, people make decisions by comparing the costs and benefits of their options: What do I gain? What do I lose? Ideally, they get a chance to make fully-informed decisions.

The same principles apply when making drug decisions. You get to compare what you gain (benefits) versus what you lose (harm). In our drug-filled world, you pretty much have to make decisions about drugs on a daily basis. However, you also can step back, reflect, and evaluate your own drug use to determine whether it is a problem or not, and whether you want to make changes. This, too, involves thinking about the harm and benefits. Ideally you make fully informed decisions about drugs, though people often do not do that.

Sometimes you don't have the luxury of taking your time to make fully informed decisions. Sometimes circumstances are such that decisions are rushed – perhaps there is pressure from other people to be abstinent or a sense of panic that the current drug use is seriously problematic. In rushing ahead, not all information is gathered, but there is at least enough to make a tentative choice. A rushed decision lacks the foundation of comprehensive preparation, but carries a certain level of commitment. You can't expect the same follow through as you would with fully informed decisions. It's kind of a Band-Aid ("stopgap") approach to holding things together. Despite that, people can rely on willpower to stick with it. At the same time, they can back up, think in more depth about the decision, and build a solid foundation for change.

This chapter is about decisions to change drug use behavior. Most people who get this far into this book already think that they need to make some changes about drugs and may have already begun to do so. For them, this chapter is a chance to firm things up. Half-hearted decisions to change usually end in collapse. If you want to succeed in overcoming drug problems, you need a *very* firm decision to change...and a fully informed one. You really need to understand all the implications of quitting or of setting new limits. This chapter will help with that. On the other hand, some readers may still be on the fence, wondering what they want to do. This chapter will give those of you who are undecided a chance to determine whether you want to make changes or not, and expose some of the barriers that keep people from making the leap.

BIG CHANGES THAT GO TOGETHER

If you decide to cut back or quit using drugs, you'll have to figure out other ways to cope with life and satisfy your needs. All the feelings you were suppressing or managing with drugs will re-emerge. All the problems you were covering up will spring back to life. You might have to find new ways to have fun and excitement, new ways to celebrate, new ways to relax, maybe make new friends, and maybe find new ways to manage your anger, pain, stress, and fear. It's not as if you can change your drug use behavior without changing lots of other aspects of your lifestyle. You will have to face your problems and life's difficulties without relying on drugs. Putting an end to a drug problem goes hand-in-hand with changing the rest of your life.

HARM

It's easy to see what you have liked about drugs. They let you relax, forget your problems, change your feelings, cut loose, have fun, manage your anger, socialize comfortably, take risks, impress people, and reduce stress. If you quit or cut back, you lose all or some of this.

When making decisions about drugs, you must guard against what's called "euphoric recall" – the tendency to remember past experience in a positive light, while overlooking the harm associated with it. With this type of distorted thinking, people become obsessed with mentally re-creating the pleasures of the past. You can see this happen when they tell their drug stories with glee, glamorizing everything with great excitement about the pleasure, but little or no mention of consequences. However, in making *informed decisions* about drugs, it's important to take harm into account.

You may have been around people – including ones who care about you – who tried to convince you to quit by relentlessly listing all the ways that drugs have caused harm. Maybe you butted heads with these people. Probably the more they pushed, the more you wanted to push back, resist, defend your drug use, and minimize your evaluation of the harm. No one wants to be backed into a corner. Taking a defensive posture protects you against an onslaught of negativity, but can stand in the way of recognizing the real possibility that drugs may have caused harm, or messed up your life in some way. When making decisions about drugs, harm has to be considered.

HARM-BASED DECISIONS

Many people focus almost exclusively on the harm. They make decisions to stop a particular behavior because they want the negative consequences to go away, without even realizing that the benefits of the behavior also vanish. Often this happens with drugs. People decide to stop using them because they want the harm to stop, but don't realize that they also lose the benefits. For example, drugs may have been their way to cope with unpleasant feelings such as anxiety or sadness; or to manage their anger; or to deal with sleep problems. When they quit in order to make the harm go away, they lose their coping mechanism. Unprepared for this reality, they are likely to be blindsided by a desire to use drugs again when they feel anxious, sad, or angry, or when they can't fall asleep at night. This makes lapse or relapse likely, and leads people to see themselves as failures who made sincere decisions but lacked willpower. However, the problem is not so much a shortage of willpower; rather, a case of over-simplistic decision-making (not accounting for important information). These "harm-based decisions" are a set-up for failure.

Harm-based decisions are not necessarily rushed. They are simply flawed and over-simplistic. People don't realize what information they are overlooking. To make fully informed decisions about drugs, you cannot overlook the benefits.

With full-blown addiction to certain drugs, the harm may be so extreme that abstinence seems to be a slam-dunk decision. Drugs don't even feel particularly good anymore to addicted individuals. Their bodies have developed "tolerance"[11] to the effects. However, they keep taking drugs out of habit or for a different reason: to

---

[11] *When a drug is used repeatedly, the body adapts to its continued presence. There is a diminished response. This is called tolerance.*

avoid the pain and misery of the withdrawal syndrome. This is a significant benefit to them that cannot be overlooked in decision-making.

EMOTIONAL DECISIONS

The task of comparing costs versus benefits of a behavior seems quite rational: Make a list of costs and benefits, and then do the math. After this, you would eliminate any behavior that causes more harm than good. However, it's really not that simple. Emotions play a profound role in decision-making. Often, people are driven to drugs by emotional needs that are hidden from their conscious awareness. For example, they will use drugs to "self-medicate" depression or anxiety, without any awareness of their mood state. They will use drugs to quiet negative self-talk that they barely notice. People can't make rational, fully informed decisions when they lack important emotional information. They can't "do the math." Furthermore the unevolved right-now brain gives enormous value to immediate pleasure or relief from pain. It's yelling: "Go for it!!!"

If you start to list the pros and cons of your drug use, it will be important to look within yourself to uncover hidden emotions and recognize the extent of their influence.

In making decisions about drugs, you may also be guided by underlying beliefs and principles, emotionally imprinted in your mind, that strongly influence your behavior. If you were aware of them and the extent of their emotional hold on you, you'd think twice about your decisions.

For some people it is all about their "reputation." For some it is about "being a real man" or "being cool" or "being a winner" or "impressing a romantic partner." These beliefs and principles dominate decision-making.

- One guy kept using drugs, despite the enormous havoc they wreaked in his life. Why? Because people were telling him to quit and he needed to be "totally free" and didn't want anyone to ever control him. Despite two visits to the hospital ER, he persisted in using drugs. Eventually, with the help of a counselor, he uncovered the power of this underlying principle of not wanting someone to control him. He challenged the belief that he could be "totally free" and saw that it was in his best interest to change.

- Not wanting to be outdone by the men she dated, one woman found herself using increasing amounts of drugs to prove she could hold her own. Unfortunately she dated guys who were deeply involved with addictive drugs and she, herself, got in over her head. She worried terribly about her level of drug use and only later realized what had driven her to her own addiction.

We all have underlying beliefs of one sort or another. As long as the beliefs and the extent of their influence lie outside of our awareness, we cannot challenge them and make rational decisions. If you have been wondering why you seem stuck in a seemingly irrational pattern of drug use, counseling can be helpful in uncovering beliefs and emotions that might be unduly influencing your decisions.

NOT SO QUICK NOW

OK, you look at the things you like about drugs. You don't want to exaggerate or glamorize – just be aware of them and how much you like them. You look at the harm from drugs – again, don't exaggerate, but don't minimize or discount it. As the detective says, "Just the facts, please."

Serious harm may get you thinking about making changes. However, the leap from simply thinking about changes to actually making them is huge.

Why would you make changes if you didn't have an idea or plan about how to improve matters, or didn't have a vision of a better life, or didn't believe you could succeed in creating a better life, or didn't feel you could resist urges to use drugs? Furthermore, what if you had tried to change before, but failed?

So, you can see, a committed decision to abstain or set limits requires a supplementary, full-fledged plan about how to make a good life for yourself. It also requires a belief in your own ability to succeed. If you feel discouraged by previous difficulties or setbacks, you need to take a "Leap of Power." Somehow or other, you must strengthen your Nurturing Self-talk that says: "You can do it." Often this requires grit and persistence, and means learning from past experiences.

If you're stuck on this, you'll need to seek support and might want to discuss it with a professional counselor.

LEARNING FROM PAST EXPERIENCE

If you have you tried to quit or stay within limits before and failed, you're not alone in that. Quitting and staying within limits take practice. Although some people nail it the first time (it can be done), most don't. Unfortunately setbacks usually feed Oppressive-Self talk that tells you that you're a failure or a loser, or that you're powerless and can never succeed. Fight that voice!

You, like everyone else, can take a nurturing approach: learn from setbacks or mistakes, and eventually succeed. Try to analyze what happened. There are many possibilities to consider.

Sometimes people suffer setbacks in their efforts to quit or set new limits because they lack the inspiration and motivation that comes with having a clear vision of how their lives could be better. Without passion for creating a better life, they simply revert to the default position of seeking immediate pleasure or relief from pain whenever pressures mount or opportunities present themselves.

Sometimes people fail because they've been rushed into decisions to quit or cut back. They didn't "own" the decision and weren't fully committed to change. Still others fail because they didn't realize what it takes to quit or cut back – the commitment, preparation, and effort.

More than anything else, people stumble because they made harm-based decisions to change. They wanted the bad stuff to stop, but didn't know what needs they had been satisfying or attempting to satisfy with drugs. Without this knowledge, they could not anticipate triggers and prepare to cope without drugs, or with less of them.

So if you have had previous unsuccessful attempts to change, take a close look at your level of commitment when setbacks occurred. Try to see whether you realized how hard it would be to change: the necessary sacrifices and the effort it would require. See if you had arranged the help and support you needed. See if you had made plans for dealing with minor setbacks before they got out of hand. You can take all this information into account as you move forward (when planning and preparing for a new, successful effort to change this time). These aren't all the possible reasons for setbacks. On your own, or with the help of others, you can figure out exactly what happened in your own case. Remember: There's always a reason for setbacks and you can always do something about them. You just need determination, effort, and support. As you read on, you will find help in preparing for a new, successful effort to change.

FEAR OF CHANGE

Some people know they need to do something about their out-of-control drug use, but don't act on their knowledge. They see the harm, but resist the idea of changing. For them, drugs have been their way of life. It doesn't feel normal to go through a day, or any part of it, without drugs. For some, drugs are the only way they know to cope with intense feelings. For some, they are all that comes to mind when they think about having a good time. Drugs are like a best friend. They love them and don't want to give them up. Change is always hard; doubly hard when you consider giving up something you depend upon or love.

The smart brain rationally compares the costs (harm) and the benefits of drug use, both of which are important. Then there's the right-now brain that wants drug benefits at any cost. It gets defensive and wants to resist change. In a defensive mode, some people see the harm from drugs but try to rewrite their story. They make excuses. They say drug problems were in the past, not now. They say the problems weren't so bad after all. They blame it all on their situation (and often their situations were pretty awful). Fearing change, they want to stick with what they've been doing, and keep on using alcohol and/or other drugs. There's no place for distortions like these in making informed decisions. Distortions are a type of mindlessness that twist reality so you don't see the truth. It's not like lying to other people: You're lying to yourself. Don't ignore or deny the truth. You have a choice: Face reality and do something about it or give up on your future.

DECISIONS

When all is said and done, you have just a few behavioral choices with regard to drugs: (1) keep using without new limits; (2) cut back to specified limits; (3) quit. A fourth option, not often discussed, is drug substitution, such as methadone maintenance, in which a regulated drug is substituted for a street drug to reduce medical and legal risks.

Everyone who decides to make changes with regard to drugs has his or her own unique combination of reasons. Here are some examples.

- To avoid losing a job
- To make something of myself
- To stop bad things from happening
- To save my relationship with my wife (husband/boyfriend/girlfriend)
- To regain custody of a child
- To be a good parent
- To be a better role model for (*name of person important to you*)
- To avoid addiction
- To overcome addiction
- To regain self-respect
- To protect my health
- To gain control of my life
- Because I'm tired of embarrassing myself (or getting in trouble)
- Because I don't like where I'm headed (jail, no job, alone, addicted, ill health)
- Because I want a future
- Because I want a job
- Because I don't want to be nasty [or lonely or abusive] like [insert person's name]
- Because drugs are affecting my brain
- Because drugs are harming my body
- Because I don't want to get as bad off as some of the people I know
- Because I'm scared about my life
- Because I'm scared about my health
- Because I'm worried I could die from this
- Because I'm ashamed of things I've done

Do you have reasons?

INFORMED DECISIONS TO CHANGE

You have considered the benefits of drugs and the harm. Now is the time to make fully informed decisions. You want to avoid the pitfalls of making harm-based decisions or of focusing only on the good stuff. You also have to consider that successfully making changes with regard to drug use will require changes in many other aspects of your life.

If you already have made a decision to change your drug use behavior, then this is an opportunity to reevaluate and possibly reaffirm it. If you're sitting on the fence, now is the time to decide what you want to do.

Your decision could be broken into two components: You weigh the benefits and harm of your drug use. You also compare the benefits and the harm of making changes. This could lead to a mixed verdict. For example: You could determine your drug use is more harmful than beneficial (i.e., you have a problem), but that the negatives of making a change in your drug use (the effort involved, possible failure, the difficult transition period without drug benefits, etc.) outweigh the positives of eliminating the problematic behavior. There's a lot to think about.

SETTING LIMITS

When the harm from drugs reaches a critical level, people begin to think about quitting. At the same time, they don't want to lose a good thing – the drug benefits. Plus, if they're addicted, they don't want to deal with the discomfort and pain of withdrawal. So, they seek a compromise, and "setting limits" appears to be an attractive alternative.

Sometimes people can successfully keep within limits and minimize harm. Often these are individuals who are just slightly overdoing it. Ideally, they start by setting clear limits on each and every drug. They simply back off a bit and reduce the likelihood of harm. They may even suffer a setback or two along the way, but eventually gain control.

Many people with serious drug problems say they want to set limits and make an effort to stay within their limits, but fall short. Either the limits are too fuzzy or their capacity to resist too weak.

Sometimes they make adjustments and can succeed. However, most often people find that they need a period of abstinence before they can succeed with new limits. If you know in your heart of hearts that you should quit, at least temporarily, then that's what you should do.

If you are considering the idea of setting limits, be sure to ask some questions and heed the warning of your Challenging Voice:

- What if you reach your limit and then think, "Oh, I handled that well; one more won't hurt."
- What if you're in a certain mood and say to yourself: "Who cares" or "I'm going for it."
- Or, what if your limit is two drinks and you get angry (or something else bothers you) and you think: "Two drinks aren't enough."

Consider your history with staying within limits: Have you tried to control your drug use over a sustained period of time before? How did that work out?

Sometimes people try to set limits and repeatedly exceed them. After each episode they vow, "This time it will be different." The Challenging Voice must stay alert to this pattern and all the other pitfalls. If setting limits is your choice and you succeed, then good for you. On the other hand, if you tried and can't make it work, you still have the option of quitting.

KEEPING ONE DRUG (OR MORE)

Not wanting to give up on all options, some people decide to eliminate one or more drugs and stick with one or more other ones. "OK. No more meth or coke. But I'll still smoke weed (or drink alcohol)." They make this choice so they can continue to reap the drug benefits, while possibly limiting the harm.

This works for some people, but not for others. In part it depends on the lure of the drugs that are eliminated and on an individual's ability to satisfy needs without that drug.

The Challenging Voice knows this can be tricky. For example: "OK, you say you'll only drink alcohol – a limited amount of alcohol – and won't use any other drugs. Then you get buzzed.

You're feeling good. More alcohol is available. You drink more. Your judgment is a bit cloudy. Someone passes you a bong or puts meth in front of you. What are you going to do?"

The Challenging Voice is not trying to scare you: just an effort to get you to think carefully.

Here are a couple of crucial questions to ponder about keeping one drug (or more):

- Is it a real decision to eliminate certain drugs or are you deceiving yourself?
- Does it seem likely you could succeed?

DECIDING TO CHANGE

OK, you say it's time to change. You decide to quit or set well-defined limits. Now is the moment to ask: How firm is your commitment? You want to succeed. So the Challenging Voice asks tough questions about what you will do when you've quit (or reached the limit you chose for yourself) and certain circumstances arise. The questions start with the sentence stem:

"What happens when…?"

- you say to yourself just a little bit (or a little more) won't hurt
- you say to yourself just one drink (or one more)
- you say to yourself no one will know
- you fight with your spouse/boyfriend/girlfriend (or kids or parents)
- you see or smell a drug you love
- you want to party
- you're out socially with friends
- someone hands you a drink or a drug
- your friends are saying: "C'mon, it won't hurt"
- you're really tense
- you had an awful day at work
- you can't sleep
- you're sad
- you're bored
- you're really mad about something someone did to you
- you feel really bad and want to change your mood
- you start to think how much you like your drug of choice
- someone in your home drinks or uses a drug in front of you
- your romantic partner uses a drug

- all your friends are continuing to use around you
- it's a holiday or some other celebration
- you have an enormous craving for your drug of choice
- you feel like you can't tolerate the pain of withdrawal

Take a little time. You could probably compose your own questions that would describe thoughts, feelings, and situations that would test your resolve. Challenge yourself to think of them.

These are the thoughts, feelings, and situations that may have tripped you up in the past. Your Oppressive-Self talk may be doubting your ability to succeed. However, Challenge Seven will help you prepare for dealing with them. Right now what you need is commitment and determination. You need Nurturing Self-talk that says: "I will work hard. I'll figure it out. I won't back down. I'll stick with my decisions. If I need help, I'll get it. In the end, I will prevail." You need to take a leap of power. A half-hearted commitment would be a set up for failure.

WANTING TO CHANGE AND DECIDING TO CHANGE

Let's say that you know about the harm from your drug use and started to think about quitting (or setting limits). Maybe you thought it would be a good idea. You kind of wished that you would change. You said you didn't *plan* to keep drinking or using drugs. Maybe you even stopped briefly. You started saying: "I want to quit" (or "I want to set new limits").

When you say you *want* to quit (or set new limits), you're expressing a wish or desire to change. But, it's not a decision. You really want the bad stuff to stop, but you might not yet be willing to let go of the good stuff. You're sort of sitting on the fence. There's a big difference between wanting to stop (or cut back) and committing to it.

- Wanting is wishful thinking, as in, "it would be a good idea to quit (or set new limits)."
- Committing means taking a stand and deciding to put in the enormous amount of energy required to succeed in making the change.

One guy said he wanted to quit smoking weed. He meant it. But when asked what he would do if a lit joint were put in front of him, he immediately replied: "I'd smoke it in a minute." He wanted to stop, but didn't want to give up the good stuff. He wanted it both ways. As long as he was unwilling to commit to quitting, he was ready to get high whenever temptation presented itself.

In contrast, if you move from *wanting* to quit (or setting limits) to *committing* to quit (or setting limits), then you have a realistic possibility of holding your ground in the face of temptation.

AMBIVALENCE (YOU CAN'T HAVE IT BOTH WAYS)

Who said life is simple? When it comes to making decisions about what to do, you can feel two different and conflicting ways.

- You can feel loving toward someone, but also angry at the same time.
- You can want to persist in working on a task, but also feel like relaxing and that you deserve a break.
- You can want to end a romantic relationship because of problems, but also want to stay together because of the good things you share.

The same is true in drug decisions. You can want to quit (or set new limits) to make the bad stuff go away, but *not* want to quit (or set new limits) because you don't want to lose the good stuff. One day you lean one way, the next day the other.

You feel like quitting or cutting back when you are happy and feeling strong. The matter seems settled – time for a change. However, you feel like indulging when you see drugs in front of you, or want to celebrate, or want to make a bad feeling go away, etc. The desire to quit drugs and to keep using them co-exist, but the context determines what you do.

You're sitting on the fence. The formal word for this is ambivalence.

If you remain ambivalent without a commitment to change, everything will remain the same. You will go back and forth in what you do.

It's like going on a diet. You eat carefully unless someone puts chocolate cake in front of you, or french fries, or whatever it is that tempts you; or unless you're on vacation or socializing with friends and you give yourself a pass. Not really a diet, eh?

If you want to change, you have to get off the fence. This means you commit yourself to behaving differently, despite the ambivalence. That is, your feelings may go back and forth, but you work hard to follow through on your commitment regardless of which way the wind is blowing.

Almost always this means giving up something good. It means sacrifice. It means deprivation. You give up cake and french fries. You give up drugs even when you would like them most. You can't make changes in drug behavior without being willing to persist and sacrifice.

An informed decision to change requires a commitment to follow the chosen path, regardless of circumstances. You can't have it both ways.

A REAL DECISION TO QUIT (OR SET NEW LIMITS)

A fully informed and sincere decision to quit using drugs (or set new limits) means you know what you would be gaining and know what you would be giving up. You know it would require hard work and probably mean making lots of other changes in your life and lifestyle. You know you would have to be ready and prepared to resist strong urges to use drugs. You would understand that without drugs (or with less of them), things would probably feel worse at first. The rewards for changing come later. Despite this, you fully commit to your decision and decide to invest the required effort.

One way to gauge your commitment to change is by observing your willingness to take some of the common sense actions that increase your chances of success. You tell people you're changing. You stop spending time with certain friends. You make plans to avoid tempting situations whenever possible, and to deal with them when they do occur. You identify the self-talk that undermines your decision, and learn to respond to it in a powerful way. If you're quitting, you throw away your stash and clean out the liquor cabinet. If you're cutting back, you set very specific and clear limits for each and every drug.

If you're unwilling to take these actions, it might be that you're not as committed to change as you think. Don't deceive yourself; don't say you're going to quit (or cut back), but only be half committed. If you do this, the decision is too weak to stand the test of experience. If you're not really ready to change, back off and think more about it.

Make sure you're not circling around in the "decision-to-change revolving door." That is, when you're feeling bad you "decide" to change. It lifts your spirit. You get a temporary boost, just for thinking about it, but you don't really follow through. Maybe you do a little something for a day or two. Without significant action, however, nothing really changes. Then the cycle repeats: Every now and then you "decide" to change to feel better (a quick fix), but nothing really happens.

If you are serious about quitting drugs or setting new limits, then commit to your decision and develop a plan of action: a relapse prevention plan.

RELAPSE PREVENTION: A PLAN OF ACTION

The hardest part of overcoming drug problems is *not* the physical addiction, which passes in a limited amount of time. It's the psychological dependence that results from being conditioned to crave drugs in response to drug "cues" (also referred to as "triggers"); such as when you're thinking about or exposed to the people, places, things, and feelings that went along with your drug use, or you see or smell a drug.

Certain circumstances trigger craving. It might be you are feeling angry and depressed (and in the past you used drugs when you had these feelings). It might be that you want to celebrate (and in the past you used drugs as a way to celebrate). Or you are bored (and in the past you used drugs when you were bored). Or you are nervous about something (and in the past you used drugs when you were nervous). It might be seeing old friends. It might be going to the places you used to frequent when you were under the influence. Or perhaps you see a mirror, like the ones you used when cutting lines of cocaine. Or you see a picture of the marijuana plant. Or you hear certain music. These cues remind you of drugs and stimulate your desire for them.

To succeed in changing your drug use behavior, you need a plan for responding to these cues. You need to figure out which ones you can avoid; and how to cope with those that are inescapable. The more you can anticipate them, the more you can prepare to avoid or resist them.

Another part of a strong relapse prevention plan is identifying people who will support and back you up. These people can cheer you on, provide guidance, and be "on call" at vulnerable times when your commitment waivers. You'll want to have their numbers in your phone.

Under certain conditions, you will want to work with a doctor, for example for medically supervised withdrawal; or with certain addictions, for medication assisted treatment.

You could choose to work with organizations that support people who are changing their drug behavior, such as SMART Recovery (online and in person), Women for Sobriety, Moderation Management, and 12-Step or other groups that take a religious/spiritual approach.

Changing drug use patterns also means making many other behavioral changes in your life. It will be important to work hard at finding new ways to satisfy the needs that were formerly satisfied by drugs. This requires significant effort and should be part of your relapse prevention planning.

Discussions with a counselor can help with all of the above.

YOU ARE POWERFUL

Drugs play directly to our unevolved right-now brains that want pleasure and immediate satisfaction. So, of course, quitting or setting limits will require enormous resolve, especially if you've come to love and value what drugs offer; even more so if you have very few other ways to satisfy your needs. Your craving can reach the point where resisting an urge feels almost impossible. Yet, if you want to quit or keep within your limits, this is exactly what you must do.

The difficulty of the personal struggle to resist drugs is magnified by the dominant ideology of our times, asserting that in order to overcome drug problems people must admit "powerlessness" over drugs and surrender to a higher power. This works for some people, but not most. Unfortunately for the majority who do not accept this religious/spiritual approach to their problems, the message or powerlessness undermines their efforts. It diminishes self-confidence and reinforces self-doubt about the possibility of taking control over their own lives. Compounding the damage is a companion belief that no one ever fully gets over a drug problem. This is not true. Countless people – including those who at times may have felt powerless – have rallied and successfully taken power over their own lives and overcome drug problems.

People are *powerful*, not powerless: We can do amazing things. The challenge is to find that power from within and use it. The challenge for helpers (counselors, family members, etc.) is to express confidence that people struggling with drugs have that power within themselves and can bring it to bear on their drug problems. Helpers, then, provide back up and support.

Building off the ideology of "powerlessness," the media tends to demonize drugs that they portray as overwhelmingly harmful or addictive (compelling in their chemical nature). Fanned by public hysteria about drugs and adding to it, these stories sell publications and bring profits to media outlets. Starting with a grain of truth (realistic drug dangers), they present exaggerated, scary stories in waves, first about one drug, then another, and still another, and on and on.[12] We've seen marijuana as a gateway drug; LSD making people jump off roofs; and crack babies doomed for life.

Gloom and doom combine: The temptation to use drugs is reinforced by people telling you or implying that you are powerless, and further amplified by the media portrayal of demon drugs. You can't let this stop you from making changes. If you've tried before and suffered setbacks or failure, don't take your past experience as evidence of powerlessness. Instead, review what happened, learn from the past, and make things better this time. Change takes practice and isn't always smooth and easy.

In order to move forward, you have to fight the ideology of powerlessness and come to recognize that you absolutely have the

---

[12]*Maia Szalavitz, a journalist, coined the term "drug du jour."*

capacity to regain control over your life. It might be the hardest thing you ever did (or not), but you have to trust yourself, believe you can do it and take a "leap of power."

CO-OCCURRING PROBLEMS

When asked what problems they needed to address and what changes they needed to make in order to have a good life without relying solely on drugs, people named numerous issues. Some of them are listed here:

- Many people were lonely, without a group of friends or a romantic partner.
- Many who did have a spouse or romantic relationship reported problems with partners that they wanted to resolve.
- People often mentioned family problems with their children and/or their parents.
- Many spoke of wanting to learn basic communication skills to assert their emotions and opinions, or to improve their relationships.
- Some who were parents had a very high level of concern about either losing child custody or trying to regain it (also trying to re-establish their role as effective parents).
- Many faced financial stress.
- Joblessness was cited as a problem. Some people didn't have jobs before the drug problem. Others lost them, or were in danger of losing them, due to a drug problem.
- People with jobs had conflict or other issues at their workplace.
- Some wanted to figure out a new career plan to rise above their current circumstances. Some had school problems.
- Many spoke of issues related to emotions – anxiety, depression, or anger. They wanted to learn how to change their emotional responses or manage them better.
- Many spoke of wanting to learn basic life skills, such as relaxation skills, or anger management, or stress management.
- Surprising numbers reported sleep problems.
- Often people were concerned about being bored without drugs.
- Many suffered from the impact of traumatic experiences.
- Those involved with the criminal justice system wanted to get off probation or parole, or graduate from drug court or family court or problem-solving court.

If you want to overcome a drug problem, think about what problems you need to address. A long-term successful plan requires work directed at the problems that have either been masked by drug use or intensified by it. Also think about what life skills you may need to learn or further refine.

MEDICATION-ASSISTED TREATMENT

As I've said countless times in this book, there's nothing to be ashamed of if you want help in taking control over your drug use. You don't have to do it alone. And there's no shame in getting medical advice or in using prescription medication to help you manage cravings, cope safely with withdrawal, and overcome a drug problem. In fact, there is significant evidence of the effectiveness of medication-assisted treatment (MAT).

A full discussion of medication-assisted treatment is beyond the scope of this book. Below is simply an introduction.[13] If you are interested in supplementing your own efforts with medication, be sure to seek medical advice. You can also find more information on the Internet.

If you plan to quit drinking alcohol, you should know that withdrawal could be a significant safety risk. Some people with serious alcohol problems can't suddenly quit without experiencing dangerous withdrawal symptoms that could even be fatal. When they quit "cold turkey," their hands shake; they sweat; they have a rapid or irregular pulse; their blood pressure spikes; and a variety of other symptoms occur. There's even a risk of stroke or heart attack, especially for people with heart problems and high blood pressure. There's a risk of seizures. So, these individuals need to taper off their alcohol consumption. Doctors can help plan the withdrawal process and medically supervise it. They may recommend and prescribe Naltrexone, a medication that blocks the effects of endorphins in the brain and, when appropriately administered, helps reduce craving for alcohol.[14,15]

---

[13] *Thanks to the Hamspro listserv for guidance on this.*
[14] *If you plan on using medication-assisted treatment for alcohol, I recommend reading "How to Change Drinking Behavior" by Ken Anderson for guidance on this matter. It offers valuable guidance on overcoming drinking problems.*
[15] *It has been noted that the Sinclair Method has been especially effective with Naltrexone in helping even the heaviest of drinkers moderate or abstain.*

Some doctors prescribe benzodiazepines, such as Valium or Librium, to manage alcohol withdrawal symptoms. Bear in mind that all these drugs can be misused and cause problems of their own. Benzodiazepines ("tranquilizers" including Valium, Librium, and Xanax) are also addictive in their own right. Medically supervised tapering is advised when you plan to stop using them.

For people who are highly motivated to quit drinking alcohol, doctors sometimes prescribe Antabuse. If you take this drug, you can't drink for a certain period of time without getting miserably sick. It can help keep you from impulsively having a drink. Doctors also sometimes prescribe acamprosate, a drug that has had at least a slight effect in reducing craving in individuals who are highly motivated to quit drinking (but not others). As with all medications, there are some risks involved in using these prescription drugs.

If you have a problem with opioid addiction (drugs such as heroin, morphine, codeine, hydrocodone, oxycodone), there is an array of medications. Buprenorphine gives some of the pleasing/analgesic effects of heroin and other opioids that cause problems, but can be taken to gradually reduce the level of use, thus allowing a person to quit without experiencing severe withdrawal.

Methadone gives all the pleasing/analgesic effects of heroin and other opioids that cause problems, but acts on the brain for a longer period of time. Because it reduces the ups and downs, it makes dosing a safer proposition and has been administered as a substitute for heroin in Opioid Treatment Programs (OTP) (formerly known as methadone maintenance). Switching to methadone can help reduce harm from street drugs. Some people enter methadone programs with the hope of eventually getting over their addiction. Unfortunately adequate counseling is not usually available and clients often leave OTPs with a sense of hopelessness.

Both buprenorphine and methadone carry risks, and can be especially dangerous when combined with the drug to which individuals are already addicted. Withdrawal from these drugs also carries risks.

Finally, people who have fully withdrawn from opioids are

sometimes prescribed Naltrexone or Vivitrol (long-acting injectable form of Naltrexone) to prevent renewed addiction. These are opioid antagonists that block the effects of heroin and the other opioids.

Remember, when you take a leap of power, you should consider all the available resources to back you up. Consider them, recognize their enormous potential to help, but be sure to use caution. Drugs are sometimes prescribed in a haphazard way, without carefully considering which drugs are used and in what dosing pattern. Drugs are sometimes used as a substitute for thinking about your life. It should not be a substitute.

STEP UP TO THE PLATE

Challenge Six is decision time.

What will it be?

What is it about your life that you would like to change?

What do you want to do about your use of drugs?

This is the time to trust yourself, recognize your strengths, seize control of your life, and make it go the way you want it to go. It may require a "leap of power" to believe that you can succeed, but take that leap because you can't succeed if you don't try. Most people have way more personal power than they believe they have. You can find it within yourself. You can also seek help and support. You don't have to do it alone.

Yes, change is hard and there will be setbacks along the way. But, remember the effort involved in making these changes is all about making a more fulfilling, joyful and satisfying life for yourself. It pays off big time. It can make a world of difference and you can feel so much better. That's why people do it. For inspiration, you might want to close your eyes and picture yourself happy in the future. You could take an imaginary photo of that mental image and carry it around with you at all times.

CHALLENGE SIX: SUMMARY AND ACTION STEPS

If you have problems with drugs, then you have previously made some decisions that hurt you. The important thing now is to make the best possible ones from this point forward. The first few action steps for Challenge Six are about drug decisions. You have many factors to consider: (1) what you like about drugs (Challenge Two); (2) how drugs have harmed you or could harm you (Challenge Three); and (3) how they will affect your future (Challenge Five).

First consider the harm from drugs. Pull out your lists from the action steps for Challenge Three and update them if you have any additions. Review your "Yes (it feels good), but..." statements (page 80). Review what you wrote in your Challenge Five Action steps about how your drug use could affect your chances of achieving your goals for the future.

When you look at your lists, consider how much harm has occurred or could occur. Does it concern you? Does the level of harm cause you to think about making changes in your drug-use behavior?

When contemplating change, don't make harm-based decisions that ignore drug benefits. If you set new limits or quit, you'll have to find other ways to satisfy the needs that drugs were satisfying, or learn to live without them being satisfied. So, review the benefits of drugs by referring back to your list from the Action Steps for Challenge Two. Update the list by adding any additional drug benefits that you may have uncovered.

As you review these lists, the next step is to ask yourself these two questions:

1. *Is it in my best interest to make changes in my drug use behavior?* Try to guard against the various pitfalls that could keep you from facing the facts, including giving too much value to hidden emotional benefits or hidden beliefs and principles. See page 95 (Emotional Decisions). Also guard against Oppressive Self-talk such as "I don't care," or "Couldn't do anything about it, anyway," or "No big deal."
2. *Am I willing to give up the drug benefits?*

Think about how your life will be better. Think about your reasons for changing. See page 81 (Walking Away From Pleasure).

If you decide to do something about your drug use, do you intend to set limits or quit? See pages 98-102. If you feel in your heart of hearts that you should make changes but don't decide to do so, then you probably need more than this self-help book and should consider discussing this with a counselor. It would be important to take a closer look at the pitfalls in decision-making such as hidden emotional motivation and Oppressive Self-talk. It would be appropriate to revisit earlier challenges.

If you decide to set new limits or quit using drugs, you'll also have to figure out alternative ways to deal with the problems of living without relying on drugs. See page 12 (Everything Else In Your Life (Besides Drugs). See page 93 (Big Changes That Go Together).

Ask yourself these two questions:

1. *What problems do I have to start solving to live well without drugs (or with less drugs)?* See page 109 (Co-occurring Problems).
2. *What skills do I have to learn in order to live well without drugs (or with less drugs)?* See page 109 (Co-occurring Problems).

Write down your answers because the problems you need to solve and skills you need to learn are goals in their own right. They are part of a decision to change.

The next step is to make an initial plan for how you can begin to accomplish all your goals. Then come some important questions to ponder:

1. *Am I willing to put in the hard work necessary to make these changes?*
2. *Where will I turn for support? Do I have friends or other people I trust who can help me? What about talking with a counselor? Should I consider seeking advice on medication-assisted treatment?*
3. *Do I think I could succeed with these changes?* If you doubt yourself, read page 107 (You Are Powerful) and page 112 (Step Up To The Plate) and think about what you can do on your own or with help to strengthen your Nurturing Self-talk.

CHALLENGE SEVEN

Challenging yourself
to take action and succeed
with your decisions about your life,
including your use of
alcohol and other drugs

TAKING ACTION

The first six challenges in this book are about evaluating your life and making decisions. The better informed you are, the better the decisions you can make, the better you can prepare to take action on your decisions, and the more likely you will be to succeed with them. It's one thing to make a decision. It's still another to follow through successfully. This challenge is about taking action and following through with your decisions. You could say: This is where the rubber meets the road.

Much of the emphasis of this challenge is about following through on drug decisions, but there is also discussion about following through on other decisions about other aspects of your life, including ones that will support you in succeeding with your drug decisions.

QUITTING OR SETTING NEW LIMITS

If you made it this far into the book, I'm guessing you want to make some changes with regard to drugs. If so, it should be noted that there are basically two possibilities: *quit* or *set new limits*. For some people, it's a no-brainer.

You may have already ruled out one of these two very different options, as in:

> "Are you kidding me, set new limits? No way I could ever do that. I need to quit."

Or the alternative:

> "Are you kidding me, quit? No way I would ever quit. I'm going to set limits and keep within them."

It's your choice. Some of you may decide or believe that you'd better not use drugs again. You may feel that if you were to start, you wouldn't stop. On the other hand, some of you may be confident that you could succeed with limits. Then, there are still others who are uncertain about limits. Some of them say: "I don't know, but I'm not taking chances" and others want to try limits and test it for themselves. If they can't stay within their limits, they could then choose abstinence.

I'm not advocating one solution or another. However, from years of experience watching people make changes, I have found that most people with serious drug problems who want to set limits get the best results when they first have a substantial period of no drug use. Nevertheless, others can keep within limits right from the start. Despite what ardent "believers" of one ideology or another might say about drug problems, there's no one-size-fits-all solution. Everyone is different. You have to find a solution that works for you.

CHANGING DRUG USE BEHAVIOR

If you've decided to set new limits or quit using drugs, a strong relapse prevention plan starts with a clear understanding of what happens on Day One when you act on your decision. You will have forfeited drug benefits that helped you cope with life. You may be facing situations that had been made all the more difficult because of the impact of your drug use. You might have lost friends, a job, housing, or the trust of family members. You might be suffering financial straits, maybe legal consequences. It's important to recognize reality about your starting point: You'll probably feel worse, rather than better at first. Change of this sort requires sacrifice. That's the price you pay. (Just like dieting: You don't lose weight by eating all the high calorie foods you love whenever you want them.) By virtue of deciding to take control of your drug use, you might get a morale boost at first. It might help you resist temptation for a while. However, the backbone to perseverance is a clear picture of how you want your life to improve. You have to engage your smart brain and remind yourself of what you want and that things will get better over time. You need a future orientation. Then, brace yourself and start preparing for Day One and the days that follow. Think ahead and make plans right now for how you will begin to address the multitude of problems you'll face right from the beginning and how you'll cope with temptation. This chapter will give you some ideas.

As you move forward, hopefully you will use massive willpower because (1) you possess the power (whether you know it or not) and (2) you're going to need to apply it. Hopefully you're willing to work hard because it will require enormous and persistent effort.

Don't confuse wishful thinking ("I hope I quit" or "I hope I can cut back") with a real commitment to change ("I'm going to do it"). To succeed, you will need to use a Challenging Voice – not to doubt yourself – but to get fully motivated and help you rise to the occasion.

The Challenging Voice asks: "Do you mean business?"

If the answer is "Yes," then the Challenging Voice says: "Work hard and don't relent."

It also says, "I'm going to watch you closely and hold you accountable." The intent is not at all to put you down or catch you failing. Rather it is to support you in being successful and motivate you to devote all your energy toward accomplishing your goal.

Anyone can say they're going to change: Think, for example, about New Year's resolutions. The real test is when it's time to follow through with the decisions. A Challenging Voice will keep you honest.

SHOW ME RESULTS

When the Challenging Voice says "Show me results," it means if you decided to quit using drugs, then you don't use them. If you set limits, then you stick to them. It's a daunting task. Your unevolved right-now brain seeks immediate gratification and wants to indulge, so you will *always have to keep your goal in mind.* You will have to frequently and consistently resist urges to use (or use beyond your limits). You will encounter one situation after another that could cause temptation. Your Oppressive Self-talk will make one excuse after another for indulging, perhaps based on claims about the all encompassing power of drugs; the grip of alcohol or extreme addictiveness of opioids or crack cocaine. It will be tricky, too. Oppressive Self-talk pretends to act in your best interest – offering you pleasure or relief from pain and making it sound as if there are legitimate reasons for violating your decisions.

"You deserve it."

"You'll feel good."

Nurturing Self-talk has an answer:

"Sure, I can feel good for a moment, but that's not what I want for myself. There is something more important to me than immediate pleasure."

This is when you must engage your smart brain and remind yourself of your reasons for changing. You need a vision of a better life – something you hold more dear to your heart than momentary pleasure. This vision even opens the door to rewarding yourself in the here-and-now: Every time you resist urges and abide by your own decisions, you can give yourself a mental reward.

"Great, I did it. I did it. I'm standing strong and won't back down. I'm going to stick with it."

This may sound trivial, but it's not. It's part of how you reinforce your efforts and condition your mind for change.

Oppressive Self-talk will feed off feelings of loneliness, pain, anguish, despair, and desperation, saying: "You need drugs. You can't resist." Some of you may hunger for drugs and feel that you can't make it through the day without them. However, when you take a leap of power and truly want a better life, then drugs are no match. If you have a serious drug problem, then it might be the hardest thing you ever do. However, you can fight for yourself and succeed. Every time you tell yourself it is OK to violate your own decision, it is not true. You must remember that YOU CANNOT GIVE YOURSELF PERMISSION TO VIOLATE YOUR DECISION. Quitting or setting limits is meaningless if you don't follow through.

Hey, mistakes and setbacks happen, right? Yes and no. First off, they don't necessarily have to happen. Sometimes people make up their minds about drugs and that's that. They stick to it. They muster all their willpower, inner strength, problem solving ability, resources and energy to get it right the first time. But, yes, you might make mistakes or slip. This does not mean you have failed. However, you must make every effort to learn from mistakes and correct them. IF YOU KEEP VIOLATING YOUR DECISION, DON'T KID YOURSELF THAT YOU ARE ON THE RIGHT TRACK. YOU'RE NOT. Either you need more determination, better strategies, or new decisions. Never give up. Figure out what is happening, get back to work, and be serious about it. You have the power to find the right decision for yourself and make it happen.

BUILDING A BETTER LIFE

If you're quitting drugs or setting new limits, it's important to consider how you would like your life to be different. Most people want to eliminate the negative impact of their drug use. They want: "Life without the harm from drugs." That's a good start. But when you set limits or quit, you also lose drug benefits. So, another important question is: *How am I going to satisfy the needs that I previously satisfied, or attempted to satisfy, by using drugs?* The point is, you want a good life and you need to make changes to be sure that it happens.

Overcoming drug problems is much more than saying NO. It means changing your whole lifestyle. It's not as if you have drugs over here on one side, and the rest of your life over there on the other. The two go together. If you mean business about quitting drugs or setting limits, you need to be serious about improving your life.

If you've used drugs for recreation, pleasure, celebration, or excitement, you'll need to find new ways to enjoy life. Maybe new ways to have fun, new ways to celebrate, new outlets for excitement, and new friends. Sure it takes effort, but the result is more pleasure and more joy. Don't lose sight of your goal.

If you've used drugs to cope with life's difficulties, you'll need to prevent or solve some of the problems that caused stress and unhappiness, and other unpleasant emotions. You'll also need to strengthen your capacity to cope with the problems and emotions that you can't prevent. Sure it takes effort, but what a relief this will be.

If you want a better life, don't forget to build up important life skills. For example: stress management, anger management, time management, relaxation skills, social skills, and the skills of planning a good recreational life. Sure it takes effort, but it makes your life so much better. That's why you do it.

Basically, you want to prevent problems or solve problems that could trigger relapse. And you want to learn to cope with problems that you can't prevent or solve. Yes, it really is a lot of work. No one said it would be easy to gain control over drugs. It means making a lot of changes. But that's what mastery living is all about: It includes noticing what is not going well, or as well as you would like it to be going, and taking action to make things better.

Building a better life is the strongest foundation for long-term success in overcoming drug problems. Be sure to avoid the common mistakes of glossing over this part of overcoming drug problems and acting as if it's all about willpower. It's not. If you don't feel that you could build a better life, it is definitely advisable to seek the help of a professional counselor.

MORE THAN WILLPOWER

Many people want to focus narrowly on changing their drug use (setting new limits or quitting) without dealing with the rest of their lives. They mainly want to rely on willpower.

Willpower is a great asset and a powerful force. However, it's not an unlimited resource. It can be exhausted. Often people grit their teeth and stick with drug decisions for a while, even a long while, but then can't keep it up. That's why building a better life is important, so things will improve and you won't keep encountering one situation after another that requires willpower to resist.

When you have multiple ways to satisfy your needs, enjoy life, and deal with life's difficulties, you have the capability to live well without relying on drugs. You then have more options and more of a choice about whether to use drugs or not, and if you do use them, a better chance to stay within your limits.

PSYCHIATRIC MEDICATION

Many people use psychiatric medications as an option to help manage their moods, emotions and behavior. You may want to consider this option. Prescription drugs won't fix the problems you face, but do offer the possibility of changing how you feel. Some people find that prescription drugs give them the help they need to get back on track; including people who have been struggling with painful addictions. I offer some precautions about this.

First, the pharmaceutical industry (Big Pharma) has spent countless dollars in advertising to grossly exaggerate the benefits, and in public relations to suppress and minimize evidence of potential harm. Before taking medication, follow the good practices recommended in this book: Evaluate the benefits and the harm of the *prescribed* drug (just as you would with alcohol and street drugs). Ask your prescribing physician to discuss the possible benefits; the possible side effects and adverse reactions; interactions with other drugs you use (street or prescribed); the evidence of effectiveness of the drug with people in your own demographic (age, sex, drug history, etc.); and what to look for to know if the drug is working for you, or not. Read the tiny print on the insert of the medication and go online to do your own research.

Second, don't let medications substitute for your own efforts to make your life better. Big Pharma, through massive public relations investments, has promoted a dogma that explains all psychological distress in terms of brain chemistry, as if your anxiety and unhappiness has little to do with the conditions of your life. This simply isn't true. Big Pharma wants you to accept their propaganda so you will want to buy their chemical relief. They're not interested in you making any efforts on your own behalf.

Prescription drugs, not unlike alcohol and street drugs, can alter your mood. Recognizing their limitations and risks, you may choose to use them as a coping mechanism. These drugs can be very helpful. However, they should not be used as a substitute for solving life problems. If you want a good life and want to overcome a drug problem, you will still need to take action of your own.

RELAPSE

When people decide to stop or set new limits on drug use, they still have desire, in some cases extraordinarily strong desire, to keep using or to use in excess of their limits. The urges persist. Making up your mind to change is one thing; resisting temptation is another. When you begin to make changes, you'll probably start with a burst of energy and feel good about early success. However, there are usually ups and downs. While striving to do well, you must accept the possibility that mistakes and setbacks can happen along the way.

Setbacks occur when people overstep their own limits with drugs. Often they are a slip or a minor setback. Instead of interpreting the slip as a sign of failure, it can be viewed as a learning opportunity; a chance to figure out what happened so that further setbacks can be averted in the future. At these times, it's important to make an adjustment and get back on track to prevent a full-blown relapse, which would mean returning to the old, well established patterns of problematic drug use.

In particular, if you slip, you want to avoid what is known as the "abstinence violation effect"[16] which goes like this: "I blew it. I started using again (or exceeded my limits) and now I give up." (To be a bit more graphic, usually, it's: "F*** it.") You simply can't allow yourself to be defeated in this way.[17] Mistakes and setbacks are part of life and must be expected and accepted.

Nurturing Self-talk accepts relapse as a normal part of the change process: "Mistakes happen. Learn from this one. Be strong and get back on track."

If multiple relapses keep happening, one after another, then it's a different matter. Probably your approach to the problem or commitment to change is not as real, or as strong, as you thought it was. It would be time to go back over previous challenges and review the decision itself. This could signal the need for counseling.

NOTE: Sometimes people prefer to call a minor setback a lapse to differentiate it from a more serious setback or relapse. However, in this book, for readability and to keep the language simple, I will use "relapse" to refer to any setback on the pathway to changing your drug use behavior.

RELAPSE PREVENTION / SUSTAINING SUCCESS

Because it's so difficult to stick with decisions about quitting drugs or staying within limits, it's important to think in terms of

[16] *A term coined by psychologist Alan Marlatt*

[17] *Tessa De Armond, a trainer for The Seven Challenges says: After all when you get a flat tire you don't say, "Might as well keep going until all four are flat."*

relapse prevention – a plan to avoid slipping. It's not about doubting yourself. It is about improving the odds and maximizing your chances of success. In fact, a much better description of this effort would be to call it "sustaining success."[18]

Sustaining success starts with knowing yourself – knowing what could possibly trigger urges to use drugs. With this knowledge you can anticipate risky situations and make plans to do everything possible to ensure that you stick with your decision. You can solve problems that could trigger drug use (or use that exceeds your limits), plan to avoid situations that could tempt you, and cope successfully with the ones that are unavoidable.

COMMIT TO SUCCESS

Changing drug use behavior requires the firm foundation of a solid decision. Make sure it's a decision to make changes, not merely a wish for things to be different. Make sure you know what drug benefits you are giving up, and what you are gaining. Make sure you understand that it will require hard work and sacrifice. Make sure you know exactly what you are looking for as you monitor yourself. With abstinence, you look for "no use;" and with setting limits, you establish your own *precise limits for each and every drug*. You need clarity on your limits.

It's important to remember what a commitment to change means. When you decide you're going to change your drug use behavior, it means "come hell or high water." It's easier to stick with a decision when all is going well. The real challenge is sticking with it when everything tanks. For some, it might mean sticking with it when they are homeless after release from jail. For others, it might mean sticking with it after losing a high-paying job and family trust. If you're changing your drug use behavior, then you stick with your decision.

Sooner or later, you're likely to experience the first setback, perhaps the first of many. Things get discouraging and Oppressive

---

[18]*Rick Barr, lead trainer for The Seven Challenges, most aptly suggested the idea of "sustaining success" being more respectful and motivating than the negative one (relapse prevention) in common parlance.*

Self-talk says, "Give up." Too often, that's exactly what people do. Game over!

After setbacks, you need to get back in the saddle, reaffirm your commitment to change, and even scare yourself. Remind yourself of your reasons for making changes. Remind yourself of the consequences of *not* changing. At this point, you need a challenging attitude and voice that says: "Show me that you mean business." You have to fight through the discouragement, redouble your effort, figure out the cause of the setback, and change your strategy. These are pivotal moments that separate people who are truly committed to change from those who may really want change, but aren't willing to bear down and show the grit and determination needed to succeed. You can't allow yourself to be defeated.

REMINDERS

Most of what we do in daily life runs on automatic pilot, without conscious awareness. If you want to change your behavior, you have to turn off automatic pilot and pay attention to what's happening in your life. With drugs this means paying attention to what could tempt you to use them (or to exceed your limits). Every morning and in every critical situation every day, you need to *remember your decision* and why it's important to you. This awareness keeps you alert. It signals you to pay attention. "*Stop! Think Twice.*"

Many people like to prepare written reminders about what they are changing and why they are doing it. They carry these reminders in their wallets or purses or phones. Some post them in their bedrooms, or on the refrigerator or a bathroom mirror.

Some people like to use reminders that will scare themselves.[19] After all, they decided to change their behavior to avoid harm. They find it helpful to think about the scary things that could happen if they don't stick to their decisions. I suggest you write your own personal reminders.

One person wrote: You'll end up either dead or in jail. You need

---

[19]*Credit to Frank Schwebel who found that scare tactics don't get people to stop using drugs, but do help them maintain their decisions to change.*

to stop using drugs. No excuses.

Another person wrote: You'll never get custody of your daughter back unless you stick with it.

Still another wrote: You'll lose your job. Don't drink.

Other important reminders emphasize the good things that will happen if you stick with your decision...whatever it is that matters to you (friends, family, career, personal values, etc.). You'll persist if you keep these things in mind. People won't change unless they picture something better.

THE MILLION-DOLLAR QUESTION

If you have trouble believing in your personal power, you might find it helpful to ask the million-dollar question. Here it is:

> If someone offered you a million dollars to succeed in your goal (to quit or keep within new limits), would you be able to do it?

If the answer is YES, then *you now believe you can do it.* Think next about how you would manage – what would you do to succeed? This can help you further refine your plans.

Of course, no one is offering you a million dollars (at least not me). So, there will be no cash benefits, except for what you save from wasteful spending on drugs and the consequences of drug use. Cash aside, imagine how good it would feel. Think of all the good things it would mean. Most important, think of how great it would feel to be in control – to take power over your life and to not feel controlled by drugs.

BUILD A SUPPORT SYSTEM

People with drug problems often isolate themselves – feeling like "losers" and blaming themselves for everything. This isn't right and isn't fair. If you have a drug problem, it's important to stop the excessive self-blame. Throughout this book it has been stressed that you didn't cause your problems alone and you shouldn't have to solve them alone. You don't have to hide your problems or feel ashamed.

Build a support system. You can benefit from thoughtful feedback. You can also benefit from encouragement to stick with your decision, especially at vulnerable times when you are wavering and need back-up. Support makes a big difference. There are three requirements to build a support system: (1) find caring, non-judgmental, and supportive people; (2) be willing to open up and discuss your experiences; (3) ask these people for their support. It's worth making an effort to break any barriers that would keep you from doing this. Maybe you have to push out of your comfort zone.

Don't for a minute think you are the only person with a drug problem. Look around. In our consumer-oriented and drug-oriented society, we are constantly encouraged to believe that we can and should feel good all the time. We are bombarded with messages that promote consumerism – buy this to feel good or to look good. Eat this as a reward. Or, *use this drug as a solution*. Truth is, no one feels good all the time. Small wonder so many people have problems with drugs. So, if you have a drug problem, you are definitely not alone. In most communities, you can find a support group of people with similar problems. You can also get support from professional counselors. Make sure you draw upon all available resources.

DON'T STAND ALONE

Beware of Oppressive Self-talk that promotes shame and isolation. A classic example is: "You made the bed, now sleep in it."

To fight back, it's very important that you understand how your drug problem evolved in the context of your own life experiences, without assigning excessive blame to yourself. (Review Challenge Four, if you need help with this.) Then you can answer Oppressive Self-talk, for example:

"I'm not going to blame myself for everything. I see and understand how my drug problem happened. I won't feel ashamed of myself. I've got a problem and I'm entitled to the support of people who care about me."

Oppressive Self-talk – still promoting shame and blame – might change strategies by arguing: "It's a sign of weakness to get help. You should fix this yourself."

To respond, you have to counter the idea that you are isolated and disconnected from others:

"Why in the world do you say I have to fix this alone? That's nonsense. I've got friends and people who care about me. It's really a sign of strength to stand up tall and get support from others."

KARMA

When you decide to stop using drugs (or stay within new limits), it's time for action. Your chance of success vastly improves if you have completed the preliminary work of making fully informed decisions about drugs so that you know your goals; know what it takes in terms of effort; know what you gain by changing; know what you lose; and know how to satisfy needs without relying on drugs. Nevertheless, all the preparation in the world isn't worth a hill of beans if you don't follow through and take power over your drug use.

For changing drug use behavior, I recommend **KARMA**, an acronym that will be explained on this and the following pages. With KARMA, you identify circumstances that could trigger drug use (or use that exceeds your limits), avoid them when possible, and cope with them successfully when they can't be avoided.

Here is a brief introduction to KARMA. It starts with **K**, as in **Know** your triggers – know what circumstances (feelings, thoughts, people, situations) create an urge to use drugs. You also want to know the *pattern of circumstances* that generally lead to triggering events so that you can stop the progression.

The first **A** in KARMA stands for **Avoid**; as in avoid situations that could trigger drug use. If you know you're at risk of using (or exceeding your limits) in certain situations, or under certain conditions, or with certain people, then you plan to avoid them whenever possible.

The **R** in KARMA stands for **Resist**, as in resist urges to use and don't surrender to temptation. You can't prevent or avoid all temptation, so you must be prepared to resist it. A big part of this is planning ahead; anticipating possible temptations and being ready to deal with them. Remind yourself of your decisions. Remain vigilant. When tempted, remind yourself of options, such as – leaving a high-risk situation; engaging in an alternative behavior; or calling a support person. You can also use a life skill to resist urges. For example: When tense, you can use deep breathing to relax. When angry, you can use anger management.[20]

M stands for **Monitor**. You need to watch yourself with ruthless honesty. You need to monitor yourself. Every day, remind yourself of your decision and then watch to see what you actually do. In counseling, people have the added advantage of knowing that someone else who cares will be watching, reminding them of their choices and discussing their progress.

The second **A** stands for **Accountability**. You need to hold yourself accountable. This means ensuring that you are doing *exactly what you said you were going to do.* Don't settle for less. Change is not always smooth and easy. As you monitor your behavior, you want to watch for mistakes and setbacks. When they occur, the goal is to learn from them so they won't repeat. You may have to increase your effort. If the same problems keep happening, you have to re-evaluate your decision and level of commitment to it.

KNOW YOUR TRIGGERS: Uncovering What Causes Urges

Digging deeper, start with the **K** in **K**ARMA, which stands for **Know** your triggers. That is, identify the circumstances that create urges to use drugs (or exceed your limits). Once you know your triggers, you can take action to prevent relapse and sustain success.

A review of Challenge Two sheds light on this. (If you've jumped ahead from Challenge One to this challenge, now is a good time to go back to Challenge Two.) When you know what you like about drugs, your triggers to use them become obvious. So if you use drugs to feel comfortable in social situations, then feeling anxious in social situations would be a trigger. If you use drugs to fall asleep at night, then tossing and turning after getting in bed would be a trigger. Think about what led you to use drugs in the past. Whatever triggered you in the past will probably tempt you now.

You can also learn about triggers "as you go," paying attention

---

[20] *You can learn life skills in counseling or from self-help groups, books or websites.*

in your daily life and noting the circumstances that tempt you to use drugs or exceed your limits.

If you do have a relapse, you can learn from that experience as well, by identifying what trigger set it off.

The following questions can help you think through your experiences and identify your personal triggers:

- What feelings trigger my drug use? (For example: when I feel sad, angry, bored, or worried)
- What circumstances/situations trigger my drug use? (For example: trouble at work; trouble sleeping at night; a certain time of day; when I have an argument; when I'm nervous about something; when I go to parties; when I visit certain friends; when I listen to certain music; when I'm tired; when I gamble; when I'm stressed; when I'm overwhelmed)
- What self-talk triggers my drug use? (For example: "Go have fun. You deserve it. You need it. You'll feel good. You'll relax. Just once. Nothing bad will happen.")
- What moods (feelings that persist for a while) trigger my drug use? (For example: anxious, lonely, depressed)
- Which people? (For example: particular friends, co-workers or classmates; family members; a romantic partner/spouse)
- What places? (For example: work, home, school, bar/restaurant, neighborhood hangouts)

Usually more than one factor combine to trigger drug use. What you feel, what you think, and what is happening combine to create an urge to drink or do drugs.

As you review your drug use, you'll see which triggers pop up most often and which ones are the hardest to resist. Take note. Write them down. You'll want to be prepared to deal with them without relapsing (and you'll get some help with this, later in the chapter).

KNOW YOUR TRIGGERS: Think-Ahead Survey

When you **K**now your triggers (the **K** in **K**ARMA), you can remain vigilant for them; looking at the immediate situation and near future to identify possible risks and triggers for drug use (or use that would exceed your limits). An excellent way to do this is by conducting a "think-ahead survey." With a watchful eye, you look at the current day and contemplate what lies ahead; identifying problems and challenges you'll be facing, and preparing yourself to avoid relapse and sustain success. On a daily basis, you ask yourself these questions:

- What might happen today that could cause an urge to use (or exceed my limits)?
    - What problems or difficult situations do I face?
    - Who will I be seeing?
    - Are there situations in which it is likely I'll have drugs that I don't want to use right in front of me?

Some of the answers will be immediately obvious. Others might require a little more time to uncover. Try to anticipate any situation, feeling, event, person, place, mood, or thought that could put you at risk of relapse.

Sometimes it helps if you break the survey into categories. For example, can you anticipate any possible triggers in the following aspects of your life?

- Work/school
- Recreation/fun/leisure time
- Friends
- Love life
- Family
- Contact with law enforcement or the courts

When you conduct a think-ahead survey, you minimize the risk of being blind-sided by urges, and can take preventive action to avoid relapse.

KNOW YOUR TRIGGERS: Warning Signs

Don't let a problematic situation sneak up on you. Try not to wait until the bartender says, "What'll it be?" or you find yourself sitting with friends, staring at your drug of choice. Give yourself a little breathing room.

To prevent highly tempting situations, you not only want to know your immediate triggers, but also the pattern of circumstances that could lead up to the triggering event. When you know your pattern, you can watch for warning signs.

- For one woman, taking a bunch of pills had been her way to

> "numb herself" when she felt overwhelmed by stress. She knew that she had a pill problem. Recognizing this, she decided to quit popping them. As she struggled to deal with the numerous sources of stress in her life, she discovered that each time before her several relapses occurred, she had stopped her workout routine and stopped planning social events with friends. These were her warning signs.

If you think back on your drug history, you will probably be able to see ways in which sets of circumstances (events, thoughts, feelings) collectively would lead to drug use. Doing something about one or more of the circumstances can make it easier to avoid highly tempting situations.

*NOTE: As you get to know your triggers, the following pages about the **ARMA** of **KARMA** will help you develop plans for avoiding, preventing, or coping with situations that would put you at risk of relapsing.*

AVOID THE AVOIDABLE: Stay Away From Triggers

The first **A** in KARMA stands for **Avoid**. One good way to prevent relapse is to avoid the avoidable. That is, stay away from the people, places, activities, and situations that could easily trigger an urge to use or exceed your limits. Make it easier on yourself: avoid temptation.

If you have chosen abstinence, then toss your stash and paraphernalia. Throw away your alcohol. There's no point keeping alcohol that you don't want to drink, or other drugs you don't want to use that could possibly tempt you to do something that you don't want to do. Stay away from drinking and drug using friends. Stay away from parties where drugs might be available. Stay away from specific locations where you might be tempted to score drugs. Don't drive by the liquor store where you usually buy alcohol. Take down the picture of the marijuana plant. Stop listening to the music you associate with drugs. This is *not* running scared: It's being smart and increasing the likelihood of success with your chosen goals. If you're reluctant to take these actions, then think hard if you really have enough desire and motivation to succeed in your effort.

If you have chosen to set new limits, the same principles apply. **Avoid** situations that might lead you to exceed your limits.

In our society, there is no completely safe haven from drugs, but you can do your best to avoid the most tempting situations, especially in the beginning when urges to drink or use drugs will run high.

Over time, you can begin to expose yourself to more challenging situations, and gradually build resistance skills. You'll need these skills. However, first things first.

AVOID THE AVOIDABLE: Self-Imposed Rules

Regardless of how you feel about rules that other people make, self-imposed rules – rules you make for yourself – can be protective. They help establish clarity about what you want, where you draw the line, and what you expect from yourself. When you want to **Avoid** (the first **A** of KARMA) drug triggers, it really helps to make rules about situations that could trigger an urge to use or use beyond your limits. This is a way to formalize and strengthen a desire to avoid triggers. For example, if you know you get triggered in the company of a particular friend, you could make a rule, such as: "Don't spend time with Michael." If you drink while watching football games with friends, "No going to watch games with friends."

Based on your own patterns of drug use, you make your own rules.

Typical examples include: No parties; No buying drugs; No stopping at the bar on the way home from work; No clubs; Leave social gatherings if someone brings drugs; Come straight home after work; Turn around and walk away whenever alcohol (or drugs) are offered, under all circumstances.

Ideally, your rules are well specified. The rule – "I won't hang out with friends who use drugs" – would be much more powerful if you also listed who is on the list of friends who use drugs. After all, you don't want to be debating whether someone is on the list or not when your right-now brain is at work, and you're already feeling some temptation to indulge.

Write down your rules. At first, they may be very restrictive.

Later, you might ease up and modify them. The rule about revising rules, however, is that *you can't just change rules whenever you feel like breaking them*. You can only change rules at a calm time when you have thought about your life and your progress.

AVOID THE AVOIDABLE: Make a Game Plan

Just as a coach helps an athlete make a plan for a sports event, you can make a plan for life events that could tempt you to use drugs or exceed your limit.[21] For example, you could think about how you would approach work with a difficult boss. Think of all the issues that might arise and determine how you would deal with them. Similarly, you could make plans for how you would deal with all the possible eventualities at a party. Think in terms of this sentence stem: "What will I do if..." Better to prepare ahead of time than to be caught off guard by an unexpected urge.

AVOID THE AVOIDABLE: Stop the Progression

Decisions to indulge don't simply fall from the sky. Rather, they are often the culmination of a progression of triggering factors. One thing leads to another and then another. To **Avoid** (the first **A** of K**A**RMA) drug use, it really helps to learn how your triggers combine to bring you to the point of no return. The earlier you stop the progression leading to drug use (or use in excess of your limits), the easier it will be to resist urges.

- One counseling client recognized the pattern that led to his drug use. When he faced a particularly difficult task at work, he tended to procrastinate. The more he procrastinated, the further behind he fell in his work. He would start to feel helpless about this. To make that feeling go away, he would drink alcohol. In a counseling session, he recognized that procrastinating was a warning sign of trouble ahead. With that knowledge, he made a rule for himself: He committed himself, from this point forward, to starting to work on difficult tasks without delay, as part of his plan to prevent one trigger leading to another and then the strong urge to drink. He reduced relapses and, not surprisingly, did better at work.
- A single, divorced woman with two children had enormous

---

[21]*Clinical psychologist Andrew Tatarsky made the analogy to a "game plan."*

> stress in her life. The ultimate trigger for her drug use was self-pity, which would culminate in her saying, "F*** it," and "There's no point." There were so many stressors in her life that it would be hard to say which were the worst. However, she noted that she hit her limit when she stopped having any fun (going to sleep at night without doing anything at all except work and caring for her children; and failing to arrange any babysitting on the weekend). So her precursor of "F*** it" was when she stopped doing anything fun. This was her red flag. To keep on track in changing her drug use behavior, she committed to making plans ahead of time to do something fun on a regular basis. This made for a more joyful life and fewer relapses as well.

As you learn more and more about what triggers your drug use, you will get better at seeing patterns and how various factors can lead to relapse. With this knowledge you can take action to stop the progression.

RESIST THE URGE: Solve The Problem

The **R** in KA**R**MA stands for **Resist**. When you make a decision to quit (or set new limits), you'll still crave drugs and feel urges to use (or break your limits). *However, just because you feel urges, doesn't mean that you have to go ahead and act on them!* You can resist...and will often have to do so. It's a tall order, so you'll find many suggestions on the following pages.

In order to resist urges, it's important to keep your decisions in mind and remain vigilant for circumstances that could lead to relapse. You have to learn to notice the urges and think about resisting them before the old habits control your actions. When problems in your life pop up that could trigger drug use, *the absolute best thing to do is to solve the problems*. That way, you not only resist the urges and avoid relapse, but also make your life better. Sometimes we overlook this ideal solution – the most obvious one. Not all problems can be solved, but it's worth a try.

RESIST THE URGE: Notice, Stop, and Think

It is vitally important to learn to stop and think before you act on an urge to use drugs. When you first feel an urge, make yourself pause for even as little as 15-20 seconds and pay attention to the situation and to what you are thinking and feeling. This is an opportunity to **Resist** (the **R** in KARMA) an urge. Take that brief moment to decide if there is something else you could do instead of acting on the urge. Can you cope with a difficult feeling in a different manner? Can you find another type of pleasure? Can you change your self-talk? Notice the urge and then stop and think! You can resist.

RESIST THE URGE: Seeking Pleasure

People often use drugs for pleasure – to laugh, relax, feel upbeat, amuse themselves, alter their state of consciousness, and enjoy life more. Obviously, the pursuit of pleasure can trigger intense urges. You can **Resist** (the **R** in KARMA) these urges by substituting other sources of pleasure (sports, picnics, movies, going to a park, reading, hiking, walks, socializing with friends, a new hobby, going for a drive, yoga, board games, listening to or playing music, etc.). It's a good idea to prepare a list of possible things to do for fun/pleasure, so that at times when you're bored and craving drugs, you have an alternative. Surprisingly, it may not be easy to construct this list. You may have to think hard to find activities that you enjoy that do not involve drugs. You may have to read about local events and experiment with various activities to discover what really works for you. It takes effort, but in addition to protecting you from relapse, the payoff is more fun and pleasure. Ideally, you will budget time and plan recreational/enjoyable activities in advance.

When you crave drugs for pleasure, you also could choose to forsake that immediate pleasure and accept the unhappy truth that you can't have it both ways: If you want to stick to your limits, then sometimes you have to deprive yourself of the pleasure you want. (For example: Dieters have to think about skipping the french fries and cake.) You should remember that making changes of this sort involves sacrifices. You have to be willing to give up certain things in order to get the overall benefits you want. (Maybe skip the pizza and order a salad instead.) It's not everything you want, all the time. Nurturing Self-talk encourages you to be strong and resist temptation. It counters the right-now brain that only wants pleasure. It reminds you that you'll feel better in the long run.

RESIST THE URGE: Coping

When negative emotions create an urge to use drugs (or exceed your limits), you can **Resist** the urge (the **R** in KARMA) by using coping skills. Often this means *finding other ways of responding to triggers*. Instead of turning to drugs, do something different. Below is a sample of ways to respond to unpleasant feelings without drugs. As you read the list, you'll probably recognize some strategies you already use. You can start with those. For long-term success you might want to learn some new ones.

Self-soothing is a powerful way to respond to unpleasant feelings. If you are tense, anxious, angry, stressed, or feeling emotional pain, you can use relaxation skills such as deep breathing and muscle relaxation. You can take a relaxing shower or bath. You can meditate, use calming self-talk, or guided imagery. If you're in counseling, some of the skills can even be learned in one session. You can find help with this on the Internet, too.

Physical release can counter unpleasant feelings. Aerobic exercises can be used to change sad moods. Walking fast, running, working out, or bicycling might do the trick. When anger is the emotion, you can release pressure by hitting a punching bag, or pounding pillows, or screaming in privacy.

Distraction can get your mind off troubling situations or unpleasant emotions: You can go to a movie, read a book, engage in a hobby, watch a TV show or movie, listen to music, go for a walk, hang out with a friend, or find something else that distracts your attention. Pre-plan how you might distract yourself.

Escape lets you leave the place where a problem is brewing that could lead to an urge. If an argument with a spouse or romantic partner is triggering a desire to use, take a "time out" for a moment to calm down and regain your composure. Leave places, including social gatherings, where drugs are present and tempting you. If the urge occurs in your home, go outside for a walk or to do something else. Go grocery shopping or to a bookstore or a coffee shop. Do an errand you've been postponing.

Distress Tolerance[22] allows you to simply accept that negative feelings happen at times, and they can be tolerated. Instead of using drugs to cope with them, you draw upon your own internal strength and inherent ability to control your response to these triggers. You say to yourself: "I can handle it."

RESIST THE URGE: Endure

When you have a strong feeling that you want to use drugs, one of the most overlooked ways of avoiding relapse is to simply notice the desire, hold forth, and wait for it to pass.

This way to **Resist** (the **R** in KARMA) has been described as urge surfing or riding the waves.[23] The urge to use (or to exceed limits) is like a wave that rises in the water. If you hang in there, the wave will crest and then subside and pass, giving you some peace before the next wave that you can again ride out, just as you can ride out all the ones that follow.

On a consistent basis, the media sensationalizes information about the latest evil/demon drug, suggesting that its lure is too powerful to resist. Don't buy it. You can ride the waves, endure craving and resist enormous urges. Keep three simple words in mind: Stop. Wait. Think. This gives you time to let the urges pass while you think about your own goal with regard to drugs and what really matters to you.

Well, you might ask, what about people who are addicted and withdrawing from drugs? For them, the urge to use is extraordinary. The concern about physical pain and discomfort is enormous. In certain circumstances, there are health risks that must be addressed. Regardless, if you are addicted, you can successfully quit (or stay within limits). People do it all the time. You can do it, too. Sometimes people use medication-assisted treatment (see page 110), which can be combined with the principles of KARMA, to help overcome addiction.

---

[22]*This term is from Dialectical Behavior Therapy (DBT) written and developed by Marsha Linehan.*
[23]*Psychologist Alan Marlatt — who first introduced the concept of relapse prevention — spoke of riding the waves.*

RESIST THE URGE: Answer The Self-Talk

When you want to quit using drugs or limit your use, Oppressive Self-talk encourages you to use them despite your decision, or use in excess of your limits. This category of Oppressive Self-talk is called "Triggering Self-talk." In order to **Resist** it (the **R** in KA**R**MA), you have to develop powerful responses.

Everyone has his or her own unique combination of Triggering Self-talk messages. Below are some of the characteristics of this type of talk, with examples. You might find these descriptions helpful in identifying your own. Notice that this talk comes across as helpful, sympathetic, and beneficial. It sounds friendly. It's very tricky.

- Some of the Triggering Self-talk seems to *bargain with limits to drug use*, such as "Just once" or "Just a little" or "This will be an exception."
- Some of it *urges you to seek pleasure*, such as "It'll be fun" or "Reward yourself" or "You can party" or "You know you want it."
- Some of it seems to *offer help*, as in "You really need it" or "It'll calm you down" or "It'll keep you out of trouble with your anger."
- Some of it *focuses on avoiding detection*, as in "You can get away with it" or "No one will know."
- Some of it *discourages thinking*, as in "Just do it" or "Go ahead."

It will be important to identify your own Triggering Self-talk and fight back with determination and a fierce tone. Below are examples of fighting back that might help you think of your own powerful responses. Notice that these responses not only address the content of the messages, but also the "messenger" – that is, the voice that wants to undermine your success.

"Go ahead, just once." Using once (or breaking my limits once) is too much. No exceptions. It's not what I want. I want to quit (or stick with my limits). Stop with this 'just once' nonsense. I won't fall for it. No means NO.

"It'll be fun." Sure it might be fun. It might make me feel better temporarily. But, don't do me any favors. It's not what I want. I want

to quit (or stick to my limits). You can't trick me into relapsing.

"No one will know." Sure, maybe no one will know. But, someone might find out. Anyway, I decided to quit (or to stick to my limits). So the issue isn't whether I can get away with it or not. You're a distraction, trying to mess me up. I won't let you throw me off course.

"You can't resist." Guess what? You're wrong. I *can* resist. Don't underestimate me. I will not use (or break my limits). I'm taking charge of my life.

RESIST THE URGE: Answer The Triggering Self-Talk, Part 2

A fight against Triggering Self-talk sometimes requires a little back and forth arguing before you can see what's happening and gain the upper hand.

For example, when you don't want to drink, Triggering Self-talk says, "Go ahead. Have a drink."

Because you don't want to do this, you simply say "NO."

The Triggering Self-talk says, "It won't kill you."

"I know it won't kill me," you answer, "but I don't want to drink."

"Well, it won't cause a disaster, either" it says.

"It might not cause a disaster, but it would still be a problem."

"Well," it says, "everyone else will be drinking. It's kind of expected that you'll join in. Isn't that what you do?"

"This is what I did in the old days. I don't want to do it now."

"Admit it," says the Triggering Self-talk. "You do kind of want to drink, don't you?"

You can see where this is leading. The Triggering Self-talk is always on the attack, trying to entice you to abandon your decision. For every answer you give, it will come up with another assertion designed to wear you out and get you to cave in. It's a gnawing, persistent presence, attempting to undermine your effort. Think how angry you would feel toward another person (besides yourself) who tried to pressure you in this way. You can't allow your own self-talk to do this to you.

Once you recognize the strategy of the Triggering Self-talk, you can see that no defensive response to its challenge will make a difference. You've got to counteract the premise. It's time to get angry and land a knockout punch.

"I see what you're up to. You know that I've decided not to drink and you're trying to get me to do exactly what I don't want to do. I won't let you undermine me. You can't wear me out with all your stupid arguments. I won't listen to them anymore. Shut up and get lost!"

Triggering Self-talk continues, with a last gasp: "But, you know…"

Nurturing Self-talk interrupts: "Shut up!!"

You have to recognize that Triggering Self-talk is not rational and won't relent unless you take the offensive against it. If you find yourself going back and forth in your mind with rational arguments, you'll probably eventually succumb to pressure. Triggering Self-talk will dominate. The only way to stop the relentless pressure to use drugs is to get angry with the Triggering Self-talk – fight for yourself and tell it to get lost or shut up. You've got to "raise your voice."

RESIST THE URGE: Present Self And Future Self

One of the trickier forms of Triggering Self-talk gets you thinking that you can get away with something today because you will be different in the future.[24]

"I'm going to indulge right now and I'll get back on track tomorrow."

---

[24] *I first read about "future self" in Kelly McGonigal's helpful and powerful book, 'The Willpower Instinct.'*

It's like you have two versions of yourself. Version one is your present self. Version two is your future self.

At a moment of temptation or vulnerability, your present self wants to do drugs. You figure it's OK to make an exception because you imagine your future self, tomorrow, having the ability to resist. So, you go ahead and indulge. You think that your future self will have willpower that the present self doesn't have. How convenient! Tomorrow I'll stick with my drug decision. It's like tomorrow I'll start exercising. Tomorrow I'll diet. Future self is perfect. We think of our future self as a different person, expecting this person to do what our present self won't do. We forget that our future self will have the same thoughts and feelings that our current self has.

Basically, we idealize the future self. But when we get to the future, our future self is nowhere to be found. We're the same old person, behaving in the same old way. So, when tempted to go against your own decision in the current moment because you expect things will be different in the future, remind yourself you will feel the same way tomorrow. You will be the same person you are today. Don't wait for the future to succeed in your goals. Stick with them now!

RESIST THE URGE: Get Support

At vulnerable times, when you want to avoid relapse, seek out and draw upon the *support of others*. This is an important way to **Resist** (the **R** in KARMA) urges to use drugs. Start thinking right away about who will support you and in what ways they could help. Make a list.

Your Oppressive Self-talk will attempt to undermine you. It might say: "Now when you are feeling weak is not the time to burden people with your troubles. It's not fair to them."

Nurturing Self-talk sees right through this argument: "This is precisely the time to turn for support – when you need it. People who care about you will want to help."

You can talk with friends, or a designated support person, or a counselor *to solve problems that could trigger drug use.* You can also call, contact, or visit a support person *to help you resist immediate urges* to use (or exceed your limits). Community support groups are another valuable resource that you could draw upon to maintain success. If you try one and don't find it helpful, try another. Look around. Get support!

RESIST THE URGE: Beware Of Phony Rewards

Every time you use drugs, you get some sort of gratification/ reinforcement (pleasure or relief from pain). So, you are strongly programmed to go back for more. Bearing this in mind, it's a small victory every time you resist an urge to use drugs (or exceed your limit). You won't get M&Ms™ or a million bucks as a reward, but you would be wise to give yourself positive reinforcement and cheer yourself on.

However, beware of one of the biggest pitfalls in behavior change, which is *rewarding success with a license to stray from your chosen course of action.*

It's like people wanting to lose weight who eat a salad for lunch, but then reward themselves with dessert. They won't accomplish their goal.

If you chose abstinence and resist getting high on one occasion, but reward your success by getting high the next time, you won't achieve your goal. Like the guy who was on the verge of getting off probation after three "drug-free" months and then celebrated his long-term success by getting high ... and, unfortunately, got caught in a random drug screen.

There's a very important distinction to make: You want to recognize success ... and allow for setbacks and mistakes. However, *you can't reward success by giving yourself permission to deviate from your goal.* That's different and it's self-defeating. This type of "phony reward" undermines your efforts. Be very alert to Oppressive Self-talk that says: "You deserve it. This is your reward for success." Incredibly sneaky messages of this sort make you think you are rewarding yourself when actually you are sabotaging your own plans.

The best defense against these phony rewards is reminding yourself of your goal. For example: Your goal is to lose weight, not to turn down one high-calorie meal. Your goal is to maintain control of your drug use on an on-going basis, not just from time-to-time. Reminding yourself of your goal helps you recognize that phony rewards are self-defeating. They are the downfall of many well-intentioned individuals. So, beware of them. Reminding yourself of goals will help you **Resist** (the **R** in KARMA) the urge to use drugs. You can recognize your success without giving yourself permission to do something that would undermine your effort to change.

Bear in mind, your biggest reward is that your life is getting better.

RESIST THE URGE: Reward Your Success

I wish I could recommend nurturing self-talk that says only yummy stuff like: "Great job. Wow. Way to go." Unfortunately, the right-now brain often seizes upon positivity as an occasion to say: "You did what you need to be doing. Now you can do what you feel like doing." And that spells trouble.

It is important to reinforce success, but I recommend you soften praise for your effort with reminders of your goal and of the work that lies ahead. Here are examples:

- Great job! My goal is ______ and I have to keep up my effort.
- Way to go! My goal is ______ and I have to keep up my effort.
- Good for me! My goal is ______ and I have to keep up my effort.

Of course you can enhance this by rearranging a bit, or embellishing in various ways, such as these:

- Great job. It shows I'm committed to taking charge of my life. My goal is ________ and I need to keep this up if I want to succeed.
- Wow – way to go! I must maintain my guard and continue with this if I want to reach my goal, which is ______.
- Good for me. I fought off temptation and won a victory. This is a small success and I must sustain this effort to attain my goal, which is ______.

Using the basic components from above, you might want to compose praise for success right now that you think would work best for you. Although you'll lose a bit of spontaneity by preparing ahead of time, you'll have ready-made statements that recognize and reward small victories, but keep the focus on the bigger battle.

Once you have your own messages prepared, whenever you fight off urges to use drugs, you'll not only reap the benefit of your actions, but also give yourself a mental reward and reinforce your success. Do it every time and it starts to feel good. It will help you **Resist** (the **R** in KARMA) the urge to use drugs.

RESIST THE URGE: Fall-Back Plan

Once you know your triggers, you can try to prevent, avoid, or cope with them. Planning ahead is an important strategy for sustaining success. You always strive to anticipate everything and anything that could happen, and come up with the best possible strategies for responding. However, you can't possibly anticipate everything, and even the best-planned strategies may not work. So, it is essential to develop a fall-back plan as the last wall to **Resist** urges (the **R** in KARMA).

The fall-back plan answers the questions:

- What will I do if all else fails?
- How will I stick to my decision about drugs when my plans collapse and I'm on the verge of using (or exceeding my limits)?

These are personal questions that everyone should consider. It will be important to establish your own plan.

A good fall-back plan usually involves making arrangements to call or go visit certain friends or trusted confidants when needed. Ideally this would include more than one person, in case the first choice isn't available. Many people think of places to go or things they would do (such as taking a walk) to exit from high-risk situations.

You should put together your personal fall-back plan right now. If it involves other people, ask for their support now: Set things up before it's an emergency.

MONITOR YOURSELF: Asking Questions About Drugs

The **M** in KARMA stands for **Monitor**. When you make a real decision to change a behavior, you have to watch yourself to see that you follow through. You need a Challenging Voice that keeps an eye on reality; to defend against the right-now brain that wants to run wild and mindlessly say: "Everything is OK."

First of all, this means remembering what you decided to do and being clear about what it means. If the decision is abstinence, then it's pretty obvious. If it is to cut back, then you need to establish and remember your exact limits for each drug. Then you double check: Is this my firm decision? Do I mean business? Am I willing to put in the required effort to succeed with this decision?

If everything checks out, then you ask the most basic question: *Am I sticking to my decision?* You start monitoring yourself with challenging questions. Everyday you should ask:

- Have I used drugs (or exceeded my limits with any drug)?
- Did I have a very close call?
- Is there something that puts me at risk of using (or exceeding my limits) in the near future?

Don't gloss over these questions. Any YES answer means that you should immediately stop and do some work on the issue. It means now is the time for problem solving and corrective action.

MONITOR YOURSELF: Asking About The Rest Of Your Life

To avoid relapse, you want to be sure that you're not losing ground in your overall efforts to build a good life. You should ask:

- Have I stopped working on important issues that support my decision with regard to drugs, such as solving problems that cause stress (instead of letting them seethe), or making new friends who support my behavior change?
- Have I let the conditions of my life degrade in a troublesome manner, such as not getting enough sleep or eating poorly?

A YES answer to either of these questions means that you should immediately focus your effort to get back on track. Make sure you are investing the energy you need to ensure success with your decisions. Make sure you are getting the support you need.

If no one is looking over your shoulder – which is how it should be – then you have to **Monitor** (the **M** in KARMA) yourself. Someone has to watch the store! Watch closely and be honest with yourself.

MONITOR YOURSELF: Recognize Success

As you **Monitor** (the **M** in KARMA) yourself, you'll get to see how you're doing on your goals, including the ones with regard to drug use. In all likelihood, there will be some progress and success as well as some setbacks and mistakes. You can't ignore the setbacks and mistakes because it's important to understand what happened and learn from them. It is equally important to notice the progress and success. Sometimes success comes in short spurts and small doses. That is, things get better, little by little. Too often people focus on the problems and overlook small measures of success. However, it is recognition of success that helps you avoid discouragement and maintain your effort. Be sure to give yourself credit for accomplishments.

HOLD YOURSELF ACCOUNTABLE: Honest Truth

You've been monitoring yourself and now it's important to evaluate your progress. The Challenging Voice wants to know exactly how you are doing with regard to your goals. The second **A** in KARM**A** stands for **Accountable**. In addition to recognizing and appreciating every measure of success, you should also hold yourself accountable for times you have fallen short of your goals. This does NOT mean putting yourself down or judging yourself harshly. Rather, it means recognizing mistakes and setbacks, accepting them as part of the change process, learning from them, and making corrections as you proceed. This type of attention to detail is precisely how you take control over alcohol and other drugs, and the rest of your life.

If you didn't have a relapse, but had a very close call, then be proud that you resisted the urge, but take the close call seriously. Use it as a warning of potential risk...and to sustain success, learn from the experience.

HOLD YOURSELF ACCOUNTABLE: After A Relapse

Every time you exceed your limit with a drug, you can learn from it. The Challenging Voice will ask: Are you serious about your decision to change? If you answer YES, then the Challenging Voice will say: "Let's get to the bottom of this so you can get back on track." There's always a reason for a relapse. There was a benefit you were seeking when you used drugs. To figure out which benefit you wanted, you have to answer the basic question: What happened?

You'll need to ask yourself:

- Where was I?
- Who was I with?
- What was going on at the time?
- What was I thinking (self-talk)?
- What was I feeling?

Sometimes these questions alone will clarify what happened. Sometimes what you were thinking or feeling is not immediately obvious, and there was nothing particular about the moment. You might have to backtrack further and consider what had happened earlier that day. So, you go back in time, step-by-step. What was happening before the incident? Then before that? Then before that? And so on. There is always an explanation. You can also approach it with a more general question, by asking: What happened earlier in the day or the night before, or before that? Eventually you will discover the event or series of events and triggers that led to the drug use. You may find a trigger you had previously identified, or perhaps a new one that had escaped your awareness. Often the triggering event was the straw that broke the camel's back; problems had been building up until they finally reached a breaking point.

This type of analysis helps pinpoint the benefits you were seeking from drugs. For example, maybe you were angry and your Oppressive Self-talk said: "You need to take something to calm down." Maybe you were stressed from work or some financial burden and thought: "You need to chill out." Maybe you were bored and said: "You deserve some fun."

If you didn't relapse but had a very close call, you still would want to do the same analysis of what happened. You'll want to know what set of circumstances put you on the brink of a setback.

Once you see the event or progression of events that led to the relapse (or a very close call), you face the challenge of determining what you can do differently next time to prevent future setbacks. You need to determine how you could prevent, avoid, or cope with the triggering event(s), feeling(s), and thought(s).

HOLD YOURSELF ACCOUNTABLE: Looking Deeper

If prior to a relapse (or very close call) you had been successful for a while in controlling your drug use, you would want to ask yourself: Why now? What has changed from before? In addition to analyzing the most recent events, you would look broadly at the big picture, with questions such as these: Had my mood been down for a while? Was I lonely? Was I having conflict in my love life? In my family? In my work? Was I under prolonged financial stress? Was I sleeping well? Having any fun? Eating properly? Getting exercise? Frustrated?

In other words, you will want to see how you are doing in "Building A Better Life" (See page 120). As you answer these various questions, you can assess where you might redirect your efforts in order to succeed with your goal concerning drugs. These efforts at building a better life are part of holding yourself **Accountable** (the second **A** in KARMA) and are foundational to long-term success in overcoming drug problems.

HOLD YOURSELF ACCOUNTABLE: Chain Of Events

Sometimes a drug relapse occurs in a single moment in response to a single event. Sometimes, however, it is the final step in a sequence of events. One thing leads to another, then another, and then on and on. In holding yourself **Accountable** (the second **A** of KARMA), you can analyze the sequence and come to see how the "behavior chain" could have been stopped at an earlier point. I like the concept of a chain because it implies that you can break the chain at any link, and stop the progression.

Here's an example:

> You have an argument with a friend ➔ you lose your temper and storm off ➔ you go to bed upset ➔ you can't sleep ➔ you go to work tired ➔ you're fatigued and get into an argument with your boss ➔ after work, you go to a friend's house who you know will have drugs ➔ your friends suggests using drugs ➔ you say to yourself, "I need some relief" ➔ you break your own rules about drugs.

After each link in a behavior chain, you have an emotional response and some thoughts about it. This then leads to what you do next.

In life, you can't control what other people do. You have only limited control over your own feelings, but you do have considerable control over what you think about a given event and what you do next (your response). You can make *decisions* to break a behavior chain. That's why the series of events are sometimes called "decisional chains."

People make one decision after another in a behavioral chain. In the example above: You could have decided to stay and resolve the conflict with your friend. Failing to do that, you could have coped with your emotions in multiple ways, such as: (1) calling your friend later and trying to work it out; (2) calling another friend to talk it through and get insight; (3) exercising to release tension; or (4) meditating to relax before going to bed. Similarly you could have made other decisions later, at any point, to break the chain. Thinking about the progression to problematic drug use in terms of a decisional chain can help you anticipate trouble and head off relapses before they occur.

HOLD YOURSELF ACCOUNTABLE: MISSED OPPORTUNITIES

To further illustrate how a progression of events can lead to a relapse, here is an example of someone who missed multiple opportunities to nip a problem in the bud. Later in this chapter you'll read a success story.

- Ryan had chosen abstinence. It was a weekend and he was totally bored. Typically, his biggest trigger and heaviest drug use had been on weekends when bored. He knew this, yet had planned nothing for this weekend. So, he dropped in on a friend who likes to get high. No surprise that this friend knew about a party where there would definitely be drugs. He suggested going. Ryan was hesitant at first, but said to himself: "Go, it'll be fun. You don't have to get high." He got to the party and saw the drugs. He hesitated for a moment, but then his self-talk said: "Get high and feel good. No one will know. This will be an exception – just tonight." Next thing he knew, he was using drugs.

Let's look at the missed opportunities that could have nipped this in the bud. Ideally, with long-term prevention Ryan would have already been working on expanding his recreational interests and social life. He would have established a base of friends with whom he could have fun without using drugs.

OK, he didn't do that, but short-term prevention still gave him an opportunity to stop the progression to drug use. He could have planned ahead. He could have planned his upcoming weekend in such a way that he would not get bored.

OK, he failed to do that. He could still follow the rule that he established to protect himself from relapse: "No hanging out with certain friends who will likely trigger drug use."

OK, he didn't do that. He visited his drug-using friend. He could still have followed the next rule he set up to protect himself from relapse: "No going to parties."

OK, he neglected to do that and now found himself at a party with his favorite drugs in clear sight.

His self-talk said: "No one will know. Tonight will be an exception, then I'll stop again."

He knew how to answer that: "I'm not making exceptions. I need to do the hard work of sticking with my decision. My goal is long-term abstinence. Exceptions get me in trouble."

OK, he didn't do that. There was still one last line of defense to stop the progression: His fall-back plan: Leave and call a support person. But, he didn't do that either.

HOLD YOURSELF ACCOUNTABLE: Pinpoint Problems

Relapses are normal and often part of the change process. Without guilt or shame, you can study what happened with a relapse, reaffirm your goal, and make new plans for the future so that you'll be less likely to repeat mistakes. As time progresses, you'll identify the chain of events and triggers that put you most at risk and can develop plans and strategies to succeed with your goal.

The ultimate question in holding yourself **Accountable** (the second **A** in KARMA) is: Am I succeeding with my goal? If time and time again you keep relapsing and don't see any improvements, then you need to re-assess the situation. There's either a problem with the decision or with the action that followed it. Your Challenging Voice wants to get to the bottom of this so that you can succeed. It will ask tough questions. Some will be about your decision and your commitment to change:

- Are you *really* willing to give up drug benefits; to live life without drugs or with new limits on your use? Think of all the "good stuff" (drug benefits) you will be sacrificing.
- Are you *really* willing to invest the effort it takes to succeed? This includes learning new skills and changing your life in many substantial ways?
- Are you *really* willing to stop yourself; to cope with or tolerate the distress, discomfort, and pain of not using drugs as you had in the past?
- Are you *really* determined to persist when you suffer setbacks along the way?

You might discover that you had not fully committed to change. Maybe you wanted to change but weren't ready for it. Maybe you didn't realize all you would be sacrificing or how stressful, painful, and difficult it would be. Maybe your decision was unrealistic. For example: setting limits may be unrealistic for you; or maybe you thought you could keep using a certain drug and it's not working out. At this point, you can rethink your decision and either change your mind or reaffirm your commitment. For help on this, you could review Challenges One through Six.

If the decision to change stands, the Challenging Voice will ask tough questions about your follow through and evidence of commitment; trying to determine where you are falling short and need to boost your efforts.

- What triggers (emotions, thoughts, situations) are leading to relapse?
- How do you need to change your responses to these triggers?
- Have you devoted enough energy to this: pressed yourself hard enough; toughened up and been willing to absorb the hard knocks; invested the energy?
- Have you been keeping your goal (and reasons for setting the goal) in mind with regular reminders?
- Have you stopped excusing behavior you shouldn't excuse?
- Have you worked on the underlying problems you need to solve?
- Have you learned the life or coping skills you need to be learning?

- Have you developed and used a support network?
- Have you identified the Oppressive Self-talk that encourages you to exceed your limits, and been able to fight it?
- Has your Nurturing Self-talk allowed you to learn from setbacks along the way?

If you've done all this to the best of your ability, then it will be imperative to get additional help. I recommend speaking with a professional counselor who could review your efforts, and identify and help rectify the problems that have held you back. Use all available resources. With proper support, everyone can take a leap of power and control their lives and their use of alcohol and other drugs.

NOTE ABOUT COUNSELING:

If you are in counseling or seeking counseling, I hope you are finding (or will find) a person or program that:

- treats you warmly and with total respect
- listens without making negative judgments, and understands your reasons for using drugs
- has a basic knowledge of drug pharmacology and drug problems
- sees the connection between drug problems and the rest of your life
- balances discussion about drugs and the rest of your life (not all of one and none of the other)
- supports you in making your own decisions and evaluating your own progress
- helps you solve problems, learn skills, and build a better life so that you can find new ways to satisfy needs without relying on drugs
- believes in your power to change and control your life
- supports you in deciding whether to use medication-assisted treatment

Hopefully this list will help guide you in your search for a good counseling professional and/or provide a basis for clarifying your needs and expectations in a therapeutic relationship.

RELAPSE PREVENTION: SUSTAINED SUCCESS

Here's an example of successful relapse prevention. Brittany had chosen abstinence from alcohol and realized that her highest-risk time for drinking was at home, in the evenings after stressful work days when she would calm down with some drinks. Her self-talk would say: "Go ahead, drink. Reward yourself."

Her long-term relapse prevention planning started by identifying the big issues at work that were causing stress. She began to solve some simple problems at her workplace, but still held out the possibility that she would look for another job if things didn't continue to improve.

She made a few changes in her daily work routine that included figuring out ways to find little islands of peace on the job when the stress mounted (bathroom trips and chatting with certain co-workers).

She listed the coping skills for stress that she already knew, such as listening to music and jogging. She also decided to learn deep breathing exercises to help her relax.

Brittany made a list of relaxing and pleasurable activities that she might enjoy after a hard day of work, some with family or friends, and some alone. It was not a long list, but it was a beginning.

She knew the self-talk that lured her into drug use in the past. She started rehearsing powerful responses. When her self-talk said "Go ahead, reward yourself," she would answer with: "I'm not going to drink. That's what gets me in trouble. It's no reward. It's a problem. I'm going to think of a real reward that doesn't get me in trouble, or do something else. I won't drink."

She threw away the alcohol she had at home. For her fall-back plan, she picked the person she would call if she got very tempted to drink. She knew this friend would always have her phone with her.

For short-term prevention, Brittany began to think about what she could do to reduce stress after work. Each day, she scheduled plans for the after-work hours. Her plans included going to the gym, and seeing a couple of friends and family members who supported her abstinence. She started managing stress with different strategies. If she felt stressed at home, she would either listen to soothing music or go out for exercise or go visit someone who supported her abstinence. Each day she reminded herself of her decision: why she decided to change and the ways a relapse would damage her. Each day she reminded herself of the triggering self-talk that could trip her up, and of her rebuttal.

At the time of this writing, she has sustained success for eight months and not relapsed once.

GOOD LIFE AND GOOD KARMA

Even though you only have limited control over the circumstances of your life, you have full control over how you respond to them. You can most definitely make your own decisions and control your use of alcohol and other drugs. It's hard work that requires commitment, intense effort, and persistence. You can also gain a great deal of mastery over your own life by taking action to improve what is not going well, or as well as you would like it to be going. My message has been "You can do it" and my hope has been that reading this book helps you succeed. I hope you feel inspired, will treat yourself kindly, and will seek and find caring people to support you as you take a leap of power. Here's wishing you a good life and good KARMA.

CHALLENGE SEVEN: SUMMARY AND ACTION STEPS

All of Challenge Seven is about taking action to follow through on decisions about your life and drug use.

The first suggestion is to write a list of all your **decisions** about drugs and other issues that you want to work on.

It's important to build a better life. Below are action steps that may look easy on paper, but really require enormous effort. Don't brush this work aside. It's as important as willpower in overcoming drug problems. See "Building A Better Life" (page 120) and "More Than Willpower" (page 121).

- Write down the life changes that you need to make to live well without drugs, or with new limits.
- Write down the skills you need to learn (or further develop) to live well without drugs, or with new limits.
- Construct plans for how you will succeed in making the changes and learning the skills you listed. Get counseling if you need professional help.

Next come the "Reminders" (page 125) of what changes you want to make and why you want to make them. Your reasons will include a list of all the harm (past, present, and possibly future) from your drug use.

- Remind yourself of the bad things that will happen if you *don't* change.
- Remind yourself of the good things that will happen if you *do* change.

The list should be written down and carried with you to remember why you are investing so much energy to make the change. A copy can be posted on your refrigerator or by your bedside or on your bathroom mirror, or in your phone. It's important to review this list on a regular basis. If you don't pay attention to it, your right-now brain will fill the void and you'll go back to old habits.

With your goal clearly in mind, your action steps will correspond to the key components of **KARMA**.

You need to **Know** your triggers. Refer to "Challenge Two: Summary And Action Steps" on pages 39-41 and to "Know Your Triggers," on pages 129-132.

Identify the Oppressive Self-talk that gets you in trouble, and develop powerful responses to it. See "Resist The Urge: Answer The Self-Talk" on pages 139-141.

Write down your fall-back plan and carry it with you. See page 145.

Figure out which situations and which people you will **Avoid**. See pages 132-135.

Think about your plan for **Resisting** urges, which may include solving problems; learning to tolerate and accept negative feelings; and practicing various coping strategies. See pages 135-145.

As stated throughout this book, you don't have to do this alone. There is support available: support groups, friends, other people you trust, and counselors with advanced skills who can work with you.

Figure out who will be in your support network, request their help, and get contact information.

After decisions to change are made, **Monitoring** begins so that you can hold yourself accountable.

This means knowing your plans and watching to see that you are being successful with them. Make sure you are solving the problems you chose to address and learning the skills you decided to learn. If you are stuck, get help.

With drugs, reminding and monitoring should be a daily occurrence. You will want to ask yourself three crucial questions:

For people who decided to quit:
- Did I use alcohol or any other drug I decided to quit?
- Did I have a very close call?
- Is there something that would put me at risk of drinking or using any other drug I quit between now and tomorrow, or in the near future?

For people who decided to set new limits:
- Did I exceed my limit with alcohol or any other drug?
- Did I have a very close call to exceeding a limit?
- Is there something that would put me at risk of exceeding any limit between now and tomorrow, or in the near future?

Hold yourself **Accountable**!! If you answer YES to any of the three questions, then that's an issue you need to work on immediately. This can be on your own, with the support of a person you trust, or with a counselor.

If you persistently can't stick with your own decisions, then it is important to go back through these challenges, re-evaluate your decision and your commitment to it. If you're still stuck, get more help. Remember, this book is educational and not a substitute for counseling. If you are in distress and need professional help, go get it. Never, never give up until you take power over your life and your drug use.

FINAL NOTE: If you found "Leap of Power" helpful, please help others by telling them about it, sharing the book, and writing reviews.

BOOKS BY ROBERT SCHWEBEL

- *Saying No Is Not Enough: Helping Your Kids Make Wise Decisions about Alcohol, Tobacco, and Other Drugs* (New York: HarperCollins Publishers)
- *Who's On Top, Who's On Bottom: How Couples Can Learn to Share Power* (New York: Newmarket Press)
- *Keep Your Kids Tobacco-Free: A Guide for Parents of Children Ages 3 to 19* (New York: Newmarket Press)

CO-AUTHOR

- *A Guide To a Happier Family* (Los Angeles: J.P. Tarcher)

Acknowledgements

I have so much gratitude for so many people. At the top of the pyramid are my wife, children, parents, best friends, and teachers. My life would be empty without their love and wisdom.

My wife, Claudia, in addition to being the love of my life, has been a true partner in work for three decades now. Her presence is everywhere in this book.

My colleague, Sharon Conner, has been the ultimate work collaborator for fourteen years in developing The Seven Challenges program, and now is a close friend. Her feedback has greatly influenced this book in many respects, which include adding an increased awareness of how to speak to potential readers. Thank you Darren Conner for being a friend and a behind-the-scenes supporter of our work.

Fletcher McCusker is a visionary friend who has been an important key to the success and growth of The Seven Challenges, plus helped make my life so much better with his support and advice. Thanks, too, for his suggestion to write this book for everyone, not just for people in a counseling program.

Thanks to my friend Rick Barr, the ultimate trainer and colleague, now for twelve years. His talent has so enriched our collaborative work. Another friend and colleague, Mike Panico, has consistently offered astute criticism and led the way in testing so many new ideas. Jared Bingham has masterfully led the first implementation of our counseling program that uses *Leap of Power* and helped pioneer its effectiveness. I also want to thank the therapists who pioneered in using this book in The Seven Challenges program.

I am deeply grateful to the late Claude Steiner, a master therapist and friend, who was my mentor in conducting therapy. Thanks also to my first therapy group co-leader and long time friend Becky Jenkins. We learned a lot together and from each other.

Eric Fancett carefully read this manuscript and gave enormously smart and helpful feedback. Frank Schwebel gave astute feedback and contributed new ideas, including about the use of reminders

Acknowledgements continued...

in behavior change. He also helped me avert some serious errors in my approach. Thanks to Henry Schwebel who keeps me grounded, makes me think critically, and avoid clichés and conventional truths.

Thanks to the trainers and staff at The Seven Challenges: Brittany Simmons, Tessa De Armond, Larry Vaughan, Cassie Russell, Steve Ochs, John Izzo, Cassidi Fancett, Trish Thayer, Carina Auler, Jan Murphy, and Karen Bunke.

Thanks to Randy Muck, Sol Grossman, Esther Margolis, Al Zuckerman, the HAMS listserv, Marilyn Civer, Bruce Sales, Leo Banks, Nadine Epstein, Jess Zech, Marc Turner, Dave Lazarus, and Doug Smith.

Praise for Leap of Power

"Countless individuals suffering from drug problems are desperately searching for a way to turn their lives around. *Leap of Power* speaks with compassion to them. Even if readers feel discouraged, they will see that they can take power over drugs, and most importantly, over the rest of their lives. They can leave drug problems behind. As the author warns, it's not an easy journey. Yet, with ruthless honesty and tireless effort, they can break drug habits and grow from this challenge. Describing the essentials from his evidence-based program, Dr. Schwebel inspires hope about a better future. He shows a pathway to success, far superior to the outdated approaches that have characterized the field. This book is a must read for anyone with a drug problem."

Cheryl L. Karp, Ph.D., psychologist, expert in trauma recovery and co-author of *Treatment Strategies for Abused Adolescents: From Victim to Survivor* and *Domestic Torts: Family Violence, Conflict, and Sexual Abuse.*

"*Leap of Power* is a valuable resource—one of the best resources I know—for any person who wants to better understand their substance use and is thinking about taking some steps to address it.

Dr. Schwebel's nonjudgmental, engaging style offers a self-empowering alternative to traditional one-size-fits all approaches that often reinforce shame and stigma for people using substances problematically. I will recommend this book to all of my clients and families."

Barry Lessin, M.Ed., CAADC, Licensed Psychologist
Founder and President, Families for Sensible Drug Policy
Co-Director of The Center for Family Empowerment and Change (CFEC)

Praise continued...

"AA's 12 Steps suggest a widely acclaimed course of action for resolving addiction problems. So do Dr. Robert Schwebel's Seven Challenges, as presented in *Leap of Power*, his latest book. But what a difference between the Steps and Challenges! The Challenges can guide anyone to Mastery Living: 'a way of life that is practiced by people who want to take charge of their own destiny.' *Leap*, compact but comprehensive, guides the reader through the Challenges and their appealing and helpful vocabulary, including Oppressive vs. Nurturing Self-Talk, The Challenging Voice, Digging Deeper, The Oh-I-Get-It Moment, and other terms. The Challenges can help anyone with addiction problems leap to a powerful life that is productive, connected and meaningful. If you are looking for a clearly articulated and logical approach to resolving addiction problems, this book has it!"

A. Tom Horvath, Ph.D., ABPP,
President of SMART Recovery and author of *Sex, Drugs, Gambling & Chocolate: A Workbox for Overcoming Addictions*

"Across the nation, communities and families are reeling from the opioid epidemic. Instead of blaming or shaming people for their problems with drugs, *Leap of Power* shines a light on solutions and offers hope. Based on years of practice and research, it delivers a welcome and empowering message that people can overcome drug problems and make a better life for themselves; it also shows very concrete ways how to get started and make changes happen. This is an important book for family and friends in need of help."

Sylvia M. Yee, Ph.D., long time community and civil rights activist and philanthropic leader who has worked over the decades to transform lives, support families, and build healthy communities.

Praise continued...

"*Leap of Power*, is a timely and smart contribution to the recovery literature.

With a respectful, encouraging, non-judgemental tone, *Leap of Power* invites readers to explore their relationship with substance use and the possibility that things can be different. Neither dogmatic nor insistent, the author provides readers a framework for evaluating their substance use, in the context of their life, and then successfully making changes. Always with the understanding that there is no one and only "right way." There is the way that is right for you, and you can find that.

Written in a straight forward, direct style, *Leap of Power*, is also an important book for counselors, social workers or psychologists when they identify clients with problematic substance use but who are relictant to see it. *Leap of Power* offers a useful way to introduce the discussion. And may just be the most valuable literature therapists can have for clients.

Peter F. Luongo, Ph.D.,
Executive Director, Institute for Research, Education and Training in Addictions, Pittsburgh, Pennsylvania

---

Made in United States
North Haven, CT
27 September 2022